**ELECTRONIC
SECURITY**

C000253996

# ELECTRONIC
# SECURITY
# DEVICES

by
## R. A. PENFOLD

**BERNARD BABANI (publishing) LTD**
**THE GRAMPIANS**
**SHEPHERDS BUSH ROAD**
**LONDON W6 7NF**
**ENGLAND**

I.S.B.N. 0 900162 76 7

First Published — February 1979
Reprinted — June 1982
Reprinted — September 1983
Reprinted — January 1985
Reprinted — July 1986
Reprinted — June 1987
Reprinted — December 1988
Reprinted — February 1990

Printed and bound in Great Britain by Mayhew McCrimmon Printers Ltd.

# CONTENTS

# Introduction

It is quite common to associate the term 'security device' with burglar alarms of various types  but in fact, any piece of equipment which helps to protect people or property could correctly be termed a "security device". Therefore this book is not solely concerned with burglar alarm systems, and includes other types of circuit such as a gas/smoke detector, flood alarm, fire alarm, and a doorphone/baby alarm.

A substantial part of the book is used to cover burglar alarms and details of simple switch activated circuits are provided, as well as some more sophisticated circuits using light, infra-red, and ultrasonics.

As most of the circuits are fairly simple, and suitable stripboard layouts are provided, construction of the various devices should be well within the grasp of the average electronics constructor, and in most cases will not be beyond the capabilities of the beginner.

# CHAPTER 1

## Switch Activated Burglar Alarms

The paradox of burglar alarms is that considerable care and effort must be taken when installing them in order to ensure a very high degree of reliability, but then, hopefully, the device will never be put to a real test. In the event that intruders never enter the protected property, this does not mean that the installation of an alarm system is a waste of time and money. The knowledge that property is protected by an alarm system when left unattended can give great peace of mind.

Switch activated alarms are the most simple and common, and they are also probably the most effective, provided the sensor switches are properly installed. This book is primarily concerned with the electronic side of things rather than the more mechanical aspects of alarms, and so the types of switch which can be employed will only be dealt with briefly.

The two general types of switch that can be used, are micro-switches and magnetic switches. The former is a very basic mechanical switch which does not have a normal operating lever or control shaft, but is automatically operated by some object such as a door or window as it opens or closes.

The most common type, the reed switch consists of two slender metal reeds which are hermetically sealed in a glass tube, and are positioned so that their ends overlap slightly, but do not quite touch. Placing a magnet near a reed switch causes mutual attraction between the two pieces of metal and they come together to make both physical and electrical contact. When the magnet is removed, the elasticity of the metal reeds causes them to spring apart back to their original positions.

Reed switches are probably the easier to instal  offer an extremely high level of reliability, and for all practical purposes can be regarded as having unlimited working life (usually many millions of operations). For this reason they are the type preferred by the author.

Another form of switch sensor  and one of increasing popularity, is the pressure mat. This consists of a small, thin mat to which a couple of electrical contacts can be made. Normally there is an open circuit between the two contacts, but if pressure is applied to the mat, such as by someone standing on it, a closed circuit is produced across the contacts.

In practice the mat would be hidden under a carpet below a window or just inside a door, so that any intruder would be very likely to trigger it. Pressure mats can be used in place of door or window switches, of course, but it is more common for them to be used as a back-up system. The same is also true of the more complicated and sophisticated forms of sensor which are described in the following chapter.

## Basic Alarm

A simple switch activated alarm can simply comprise a number of normally open (n.o.) contacts, a latching relay, an alarm generator, and a power source, as shown in Fig.1. The problem with this simple arrangement is that a break in the wiring to the switches, either deliberate or accidental, will render the circuit inoperative. It also requires a twin lead to run from the alarm circuit to each switch.

There are advantages to a circuit which uses a number of normally closed (n.c.) switches wired in series. Any break in the wiring will cause the alarm to sound and thus indicate either a failure in the wiring, or that the wiring has been tampered with. Also, it is then only necessary to run a single wire from the alarm to one side of the first switch. The other side of that switch is then connected by a single wire to one side of the next switch in the chain, and so on back to the second

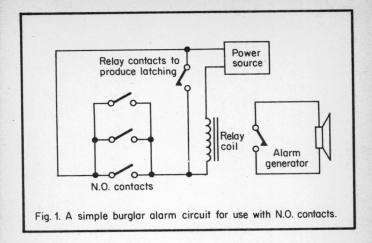

Fig. 1. A simple burglar alarm circuit for use with N.O. contacts.

contact on the alarm. This significantly simplifies the wiring of the switches.

Practical alarm circuits are often equipped to operate with either n.c. switches, or n.o. switches, or both, and the alarm circuits provided here are of this type. The circuit diagram of a basic burglar alarm circuit of the switch-activated type is shown in Fig.2. In practice the n.c. contacts would probably be window and door switches and the n.o. contacts would be pressure mats and (or) the relay contacts of some more sophisticated form of sensor, such as an infra-red ultra-sonic circuit.

## Circuit Operation

The unit is based on a CMOS 2 input NOR gate, and the 4001 I.C. actually contains four such gates. The six inputs of the three unused gates are connected to the negative supply rail so that they do not pick-up any stray voltages. These could easily result in the static current consumption of the I.C. (which is otherwise only a small fraction of a micro-amp) being very much increased, and high static voltages

11

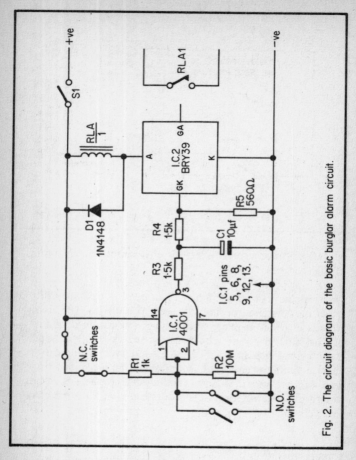

Fig. 2. The circuit diagram of the basic burglar alarm circuit.

could possibly damage the chip if inputs are left floating. CMOS I.C.s have exceptionally high input impedances of typically over 1 million Meg. ohms and are therefore easily affected by stray and static voltages. The outputs of the three unused gates are simply ignored.

For the benefit of readers who are unfamiliar with logic circuits, the inputs and outputs only have two stable states

12

they are either at logic 1 (high, or virtually equal to the positive supply rail potential) or at logic 0 (low, or virtually equal to the negative supply rail potential). Which of these states is assumed by the output depends upon the logic levels of the inputs. For a 2 input NOR gate the outputs is high if both inputs are low, and low for the other three possible input combinations. In this case the two inputs are simply connected in parallel so that the gate acts as a simple inverter, and it is quite common for CMOS gates to be used in this fashion.

Under normal conditions the input of the inverter is taken to the high state by R1 and the normally closed switches. R2 will tend to take the input slightly negative of the positive supply rail potential but as the value of R2 is very high in comparison to that of R1 this effect is minimal and does not upset the operation of the circuit. Thus under quiescent conditions the output of the circuit is in the low state as the input is in the high state.

If one of the n.c. switches should be momentarily opened, R1 will then be effectively disconnected from the circuit and R2 will connect the input of the inverter to the negative supply rail. If one of the n.o. switches is operated this will also result in the inverter's input being taken to the negative supply rail voltage. In either case, with the input in the low state the output will go high.

The output of the inverter is used to drive the input of silicon controlled switch I.C.2. With the GA terminal of this device ingnored, as it is here, it operates as a very sensitive thyristor R5 is needed in order to prevent the S.C.S. from spuriously triggering to the on state so that it remains off when the output of I.C.1 is low. When the output of I.C.1 goes into the high state, however, the 0.6 volts or so needed at the CK terminal of I.C.2 in order to switch it on, will be produced.

This will result in power being fed to the relay coil, the relay contacts will close, and the alarm will be sounded. D1 is the protective diode which is normally incorporated in relay driver circuits, and it is needed in order to suppress the high reverse voltage which would otherwise be generated across the relay as it deactivated. Although at a high impedance this voltage could easily damage one of the I.C.s if it were not eliminated.

The reason for using a silicon controlled switch to drive the relay rather than a switching transistor, is that the former, like a thyristor, latches in the "on" state once it has been triggered. If an ordinary transistor were to be used it would be necessary to use some additional circuitry to provide latching. Remember that if the switches are set back to their original positions after the alarm has sounded, the inverter will revert to its original input and output states. If a transistor was used in place of the S.C.S. the relay would only be activated for as long as the output of the inverter was in the high state, and so returning the switches to their original states would silence the alarm.

By using an S.C.S. it is only possible to silence the alarm by switching the circuit off using S1. This cuts the power to the relay which will turn off in consequence, but it also causes the current through the S.C.S. to fall to zero so that this switches off as well. With the input switches set to the correct quiescent states, when S1 is once again closed, the circuit recommences operation as described earlier.

R3, R4, and C1 form a simple filter which is designed to remove any noise spikes which are picked up in the switch wiring and which could otherwise result in spurious triggering of the circuit. Such noise spikes can be caused by refrigerators and other electrical appliances as well as by lightning. C1 can be increased in value, if necessary, to provide increased immunity against such noise spikes, but it should not be made too high in value since this would result in brief operations of the input switches being ineffective.

Note that although just two n.o. switches are shown in the circuit diagram, as many n.o. switches as desired can be wired in parallel. Similarly, only two switches are shown in the n.c. chain of switches, but any number of switches can be used in this set of series-connected switches.

14

## Construction

A suitable 0.1 in. matrix stripboard layout for the unit is
shown in Fig. 3. Begin construction of the panel by cutting
out a piece of stripboard of the correct size (15 copper strips
by 17 holes) using a hacksaw. File up any rough edges which
are produced, drill the two 3.2 m.m. diameter mounting holes,
and make the seven breaks in the copper strips.

Next the various components and link wires are soldered into
position. Because CMOS I.C.s such as I.C.1 can be damaged
by static voltages they are usually packed in some form of
protective packaging. This is either conductive foam or alumin-

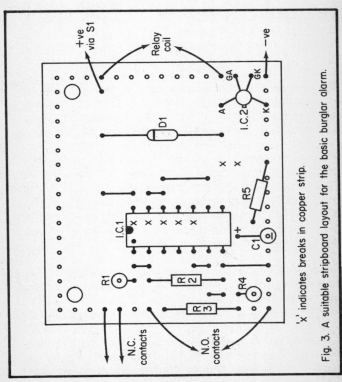

'x' indicates breaks in copper strip.

Fig. 3. A suitable stripboard layout for the basic burglar alarm.

ium foil, which is used to short the pins of the device together so that any static build up between the pins is leaked away, or a plastic tube is used to insulate the device from any high static voltages. In either case I.C.1 should be left in the protective packaging until it is time to connect the device into circuit, and it should then be handled as little as possible. It is preferable to use an I.C. socket or solder pins for this component, but as the 4001 I.C. is very inexpensive the cost of some form of holder is perhaps not really justified. If I.C.1 is soldered direct to the component panel a soldering iron having an earthed bit should be used.

Apart from this, construction of the component panel is quite straight forward. However, make absolutely certain that all soldered joints are of high quality so that the finished alarm will have good reliability. For the same reason it is advisable to use only the highest quality components in the unit.

The relay is not mounted on the panel as the mounting arrangements of relays vary considerably from one type to another. Most types will require a mounting bracket of some kind so that they can be secured to the inside of the case.

The prototype was tried with an RS Open construction PC type relay having a 6 volt 410 ohm coil, and it was also used successfully with an old surplus relay having a 6 volt 200 ohm coil. In fact any relay having a nominal 6 volt coil with a resistance of about 150 ohms or more should be suitable for use in this device, provided the relay contacts are of adequate rating and of the right type, of course.

Any good strong case of adequate dimensions to take all the parts should make a suitable housing for the unit. It is a good idea to use a key switch for S1 so that there is no easy way for an intruder to silence the alarm once it has begun to sound.

It is quite feasible to power the circuit from batteries as the quiescent current consumption of the unit is only about one microamp. This is the current which flows through R1 and

16

R2; neither of the two I.C.s consume any significant standby current, which is the main reason for choosing them for this application. With such a low quiescent current consumption the batteries last for virtually their shelf life which for ordinary dry cells is many months (provided they are reasonably fresh when purchased, of course). It would be a false economy to attempt to use each set of batteries for as long as possible as this could result in them becoming completely exhausted while still in circuit, with the alarm being rendered useless as a result. Either periodically check the battery voltage and replace the battery when its voltage has fallen to about 10% or so below its nominal level, or replace the batteries at fixed intervals, say every five months.

The circuit requires a nominal supply voltage of about 9 to 12 volts, and when the circuit is activated it has a current consumption of about 25mA. (the precise figure depending upon the resistance of the relay used in the unit). This can be supplied by any small capacity battery such as a PP6. However, if the same supply is used for the alarm generator, it will be necessary to use a higher capacity battery, such as six HP2 cells connected in series.
If preferred, a mains operated power supply can be used. Suitable battery eliminators are available ready made and there are also many home-constructor designs for those.

Suitable alarm generators for this application are available ready made, or the design featured at the end of this Chapter can be used.


**Components for Basic Burglar Alarm.**

**Resistors.** All are ¼ watt 10%.

| | | | |
|-----|---------|-----|-----------|
| R1 | 1k. | R4 | 1.5k. |
| R2 | 10 Meg. | R5 | 560 ohms. |
| R3 | 1.5k. | | |

**Capacitor.**

| | |
|----|-----------------|
| C1 | 10mfd. 10v.w. |

**Semiconductors.**
I.C.1        CMOS 4001.
I.C.2        BRY39.
D1           1N4148.

**Switches.**
S1           S.P.S.T. key switch.
Micro and (or) reed switches as required.

**Relay.**
Nominal 6 volt operation, coil resistance about 185 ohms. or
more and sufficient contacts of the appropriate type and
rating for the load(s) employed.

**Miscellaneous.**
0.1in. matrix stripboard panel.
Case, connecting wire, solder, etc.


**Exit Delay Circuit**

One problem when using a basic alarm circuit of the type
just described is leaving the house without triggering the
alarm. The usual way round this is to have a key switch at
one door which can be used to disable the sensor switch fitted
to that door. In order to disable a n.o. switch the key switch
should be wired in series with the sensor switch, and will
provide disabling when it is in the open position. For a n.c.
switch the key switch should be wired in parallel with the
sensor switch, and will provide disabling when it is in the
closed position.

When leaving the house it is necessary to first go outside and
set the key switch to the 'disable' position, go back into the
house and switch on the alarm, return outside and close the
door, and finally set the key switch to the enable position.
Before re-entering the house the key switch should be set
into the disable position to prevent the alarm from being
activated.

18

If the alarm is never to be used while the premises are occupied this procedure is somewhat simplified as the key switch will normally be in the 'disable' position, and so it is then only necessary to turn on the alarm before leaving, and set the key to the 'enable' position once outside with the door closed. Again, the key switch is set to the 'disable' position before re-entering the house. The flaw with this arrangement is that most burglar alarm systems are used at night time as well as when the premises are left unattended.

In order to simplify matters somewhat, many alarms are fitted with an exit facility. This consists of a small amount of additional circuitry to provide a delay between the alarm being switched on and it becoming operational. It is then possible to simply switch the alarm on and leave the house by any exit, as the unit will not come into operation until after the occupants have left the house.

It is still necessary to have the key switch so that the alarm can be disabled before entering the house, and it must be ensured that this is in the 'enable' position before going away from the premises. The advantage of the exit delay is that it is not necessary to check on the position of the key switch before switching on the alarm.

**Exit Delay Modification**

It is a very simple matter to modify the unit to provide an exit delay and the necessary circuit modification is shown in Fig. 4.

Instead of simply wiring the two inputs of the gate in parallel so that it acts as an inverter, here the inputs are fed from separate sources and the gate is actually used as such. As was explained earlier, the output of a two input NOR gate will be high if the two inputs are low, and the output will be low for the other three input combinations.

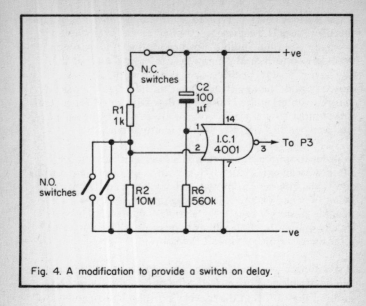

Fig. 4. A modification to provide a switch on delay.

If the sensor switch on the exit door is not disabled, this will obviously result in pin 2 of I.C.1 going low when the door is opened. However, pin 1 will be in the high state until C2 has become largely charged up by way of R6. Both inputs must be low in order for the output of the gate to go high and operate the alarm, and so the alarm cannot operate until C2 has charged up and pin 1 has gone into the low state. This takes approximately 1 minute, which gives ample time to leave once the alarm has been switched on.

When the door is closed, pin 2 will be in the high state, and so when pin 2 reaches the low state the alarm will not be triggered. If any of the sensor switches are activated and pin 2 is taken low, then both inputs will be in the low state and the alarm will be triggered. Thus, after the initial delay period the circuit functions normally.

20

## Construction

The unit is constructed in much the same way as the original circuit, but a slightly larger stripboard panel is needed (20 holes by 15 copper strips). The left hand portion of the board has the layout shown in Fig. 5. The rest of the board is not shown as it retains the original layout shown in Fig.3. Apart from this small alteration to the component panel construction is the same as before.

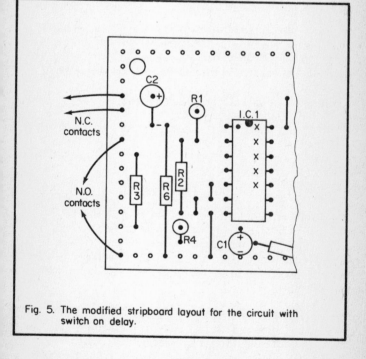

Fig. 5. The modified stripboard layout for the circuit with switch on delay.

Note that C2 must be a high quality component as otherwise its leakage resistance could be low enough to hold pin 1 in the high state and block the operation of the circuit.

One way of testing the suitability of components for the C2 position is to connect them into circuit, activate one of the sensor switches, switch the unit on, and measure the time taken before the alarm sounds. If the time taken is much more than one minute this suggests that the capacitor has a high leakage current and is not really suitable.

The current consumption of the circuit may be a little higher than that of the original due to the leakage current through C2 and R6, but it should still only be something in the region of a couple of microamps, which is still insignificant.

If desired, the length of the exit delay can be altered by changing the value of C2. Increasing the value of this component proportionately increases the length of the delay, and decreasing its value proportionately decreases the delay.

**Additional Components for Switch on Delay**
R6          560k.
C2          100mfd. 16v.w. (see text).

**Entry Delay**

It is possible to eliminate the need for any external key switches by using a circuit which gives a delay before the alarm sounds, once the alarm has been triggered, as well as providing the exit delay. This has several advantages such as being more convenient to use, greater security, and simplification of the installation.

With this type of alarm it is only necessary to switch the unit on before leaving, and the exit prevents the alarm from sounding when one leaves through a protected door. When re-entering the house the alarm will be triggered, but the entry delay will prevent the alarm from sounding for some pre-determined period of time, say about half a minute. This gives the operator ample time to switch off the alarm and thus prevent it from sounding at all.

The on/off switch must be a key type, and the case containing the electronics should be placed somewhere out of sight, so that any intruder will have no real chance of deactivating the circuit before the alarm is given.

This system is obviously much more convenient in use, and it is easier to install since there is no need to have an external key switch, and the problems of installing this are avoided. Also, having an external switch, (even if it is a good quality key type) which can partially disable the alarm system is obviously undesirable. Therefore this system provides increased security.

## The Circuit

The circuit diagram of an alarm system which has both exit and entry delay facilities is given in Fig. 6. This is based on the previous circuit, and is identical up to the load for the silicon controlled switch. Instead of the relay, a resistor is now used here.

Normally the voltage at the anode of I.C.2 will be almost equal to the positive supply rail potential, but when the alarm is triggered, this voltage will fall to about 1 volt. This results in C3 beginning to charge up via R8.

One of the previously unused gates of I.C.1 is wired as an inverter and has its input fed from the junction of C3 and R8. This junction will be in the high state under quiescent conditions, and so the input of the inverter will be high and its output will be low.

The output of the inverter drives the base of common emitter switching transistor Tr1 via current limiting resistor R9. The relay coil and protective diode D1 form the collector load for Tr1. Under quiescent conditions no base current will be supplied to Tr1 from the low output of the inverter, and so both Tr1 and the relay will be turned off.

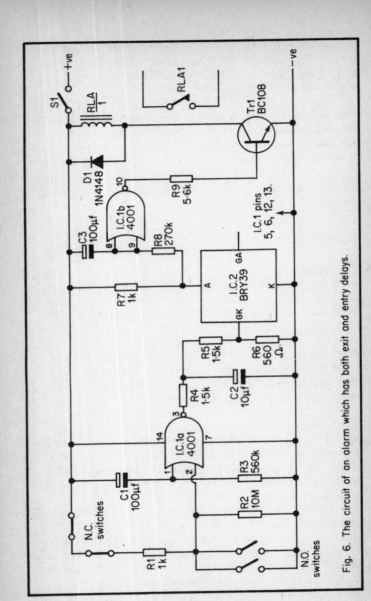

Fig. 6. The circuit of an alarm which has both exit and entry delays.

24

When the alarm is triggered, the input of the inverter will gradually go from the high state to the low state as C3 charges up via R8. When the input voltage to the inverter reaches a sufficiently low level, which will be approximately half a minute after the circuit was triggered, the output of the inverter will go the high state. Tr1 then receives a heavy base current through R9 and is switched hard on in consequence. This causes the alarm to be sounded, and it will continue to sound until the circuit is switched off using S1. Both C1 and C3 will then discharge, and the circuit will be ready to commence operation again when S1 is switched to the "on" position once again.

## Construction

The main circuitry can be assembled on a 0.1in. pitch stripboard which has 24 holes by 15 copper strips using the component layout illustrated in Fig. 7. Note that like C1, C3 must be a high quality component, or it may be found that there is an excessively long entry delay. A really poor quality component in this position could result in the alarm failing to sound at all due to the poor insulation resistance holding the input of the inverter in the high position.

Apart from the new component layout, construction of the unit is otherwise much the same as for the previous circuits.

If necessary, the length of the entry delay can be altered to suit individual requirements, as in the preceding circuits.

## Components for Alarm With Exit and Entry Delays.

**Resistors.** All are ¼ watt 10%.

| R1 | 1k. | R6 | 560 ohms. |
|----|-----|----|-----------|
| R2 | 10 Meg. | R7 | 1k. |
| R3 | 560k. | R8 | 270k. |
| R4 | 1.5k. | R9 | 5.6k. |
| R5 | 1.5k. | | |

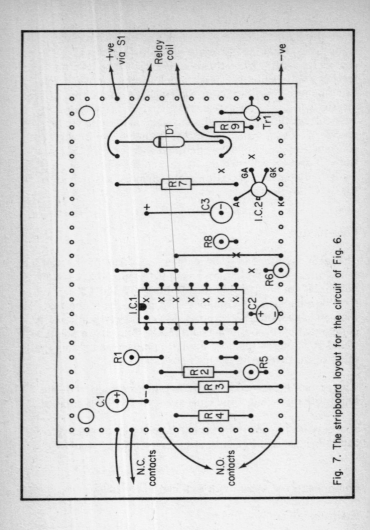

Fig. 7. The stripboard layout for the circuit of Fig. 6.

**Capacitors.**

| | |
|---|---|
| C1 | 100mfd. 16v.w. |
| C2 | 10mfd. 10v.w. |
| C3 | 100mfd. 16v.w. |

26

**Semiconductors.**
I.C.1       CMOS 4001
I.C.2       BRY39.
Tr1         BC108.
D1          1N4148.

**Switches.**
S1          S.P.S.T. key switch.
Micro and (or) reed switches as required.

**Relay.**
Nominal 6 volt operation, coil resistance about 185 ohms or
more and sufficient contacts of the appropriate type and rating
for load(s) employed.

**Miscellaneous.**
0.1in. matrix stripboard panel.
Case, connecting wire, solder, etc.


**Tone Generator**

Any loud alarm generator should be suitable for use with
these circuits, and there are a number of excellent ready
made units available. Some are electromagnetic devices which
have no electronic circuitry, and others use an electronic
tone generator circuit to drive an electromagnetic transducer
such as a loudspeaker. Units of the latter type are easily produced by the home-constructor, and such a device is described here.

Some alarms provide an intermittent or frequency modulated
tone in order to make them more noticeable. However, this
is by no means essential, and any loud alarm signal should be
sufficient to scare off an intruder, who is unlikely to wait
around when it is apparent that his presence has been detected.
The alarm should be loud enough to alert the neighbours so
that they can take the appropriate action.

The circuit diagram of the tone generator is shown in Fig. 8, and this is based on a couple of NE555V timer I.C.s. I.C.2 is used to generator the basic tone and Tr1 amplifies this to a suitable level to drive a loudspeaker. I.C.1 is used to provide an auto switch-off facility, and this is discussed more fully later on.

I.C.2 is used in the astable mode, and in this mode C4 first charges up to two thirds of the supply rail voltage through R4 and R5, and then it discharges to one third of the supply rail voltage through R5 and an internal transistor of the I.C. The circuit oscillates continuously in this manner. While C4 is charging up, the output of the I.C. (pin 3) is high, and when C4 discharges the output is low.

The output of I.C.1 is used to drive the base of common emitter amplifier Tr1 via current limiting resistor R6. The loudspeaker forms the collector load for Tr1, and so a heavy current will be fed to the loudspeaker for the period that I.C.1 output is high, and Tr1 is switched on.

R4, R5, and C4 have been given values which produce an output frequency of a little over 1kHz, but this can be altered if a different frequency is preferred. Decreasing the value of C4 produces a proportionate increase in frequency, and reducing its value has the opposite effect.

The mean output power fed to the speaker is something over 2.5 watts with a 9 volt supply and about 4.5 watts with a 12 volt supply. This may not seem to be particularly powerful, but with any reasonably efficient loudspeaker this is enough to produce a signal which can be clearly heard at quite a distance, and which is uncomfortably loud for anyone at all close to the loudspeaker.

An auto turn-off facility is often incorporated into burglar alarm systems since once the alarm has sounded for a few minutes it will have scared off the intruder and will have alerted the neighbours. This will leave the alarm sounding unnecessarily until the owner returns and switches it off.

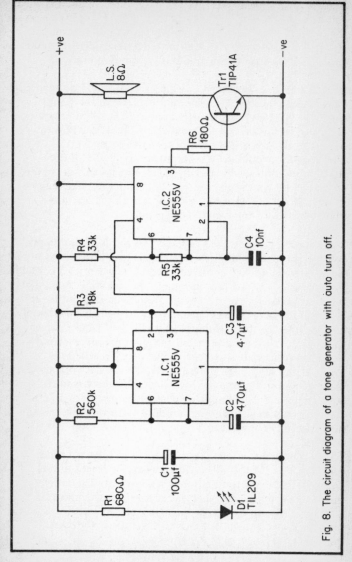

Fig. 8. The circuit diagram of a tone generator with auto turn off.

29

This can result in a lot of annoyance for the neighbours, which can be avoided by including circuitry to switch off the alarm after it has been operating for some predetermined time. In this circuit I.C.1 is used to control the tone generator circuit and switch it off after the required period of operation.

I.C.1 is an NE555V timer I.C. which is connected in the monostable configuration. When used in this fashion the timing capacitor (C2) is normally held discharged by an internal transistor of the I.C., and the output of the device is in the low state. If the trigger input of the device (pin 2) is momentarily taken low, the output will go high and the short circuit on C2 will be removed so that it can start to charge via R2. In this circuit, pin 2 of I.C.1 will be taken low by C3 as soon as the supply is connected to the alarm, so that the circuit is immediately triggered.

When the charge on C2 has reached two thirds of the supply rail potential, the circuit is triggered back to its original state with C2 being discharged by an internal transistor of I.C.1 and the output of the device returning to the low state. Note that the initial triggering of the circuit must be carried out by an R – C network (R3 and C3), and pin 2 of I.C.1 cannot simply be connected to the negative supply rail. This would trigger the circuit, but it would prevent the circuit from reverting to the low output state when the charge on C2 reached two thirds of the supply rail potential. The R – C network avoids this since C3 will take pin 2 low when the supply is initially connected, but C3 will quickly charge through R3 with pin 2 being taken to virtually the full positive supply rail potential in consequence.

The output of I.C.1 (pin 3) is connected to the reset input (pin 4) of I.C.2. I.C.2 will oscillate when the reset input is high, but will cease to function when it is low. Therefore, the circuit will oscillate when the supply is first connected and the output of I.C.1 is in the high state, but it will cease to oscillate at the end of I.C.1's timing period. In this way the auto switch-off facility is provided.

With the specified component values the tone is switched on for approximately five minutes, but it is possible to increase or decrease this time by raising or lowering the value of C2. This capacitor should be a good quality component.

When I.C.2 stops oscillating, its output terminal goes into the low state and Tr1 becomes cut off. This is essential since if it went into the high or some intermediate state a continuous high current would flow through Tr1 and the loudspeaker.

R1 and D1 provide a visual indication that the alarm has been activated, and L.E.D. indicator D1 remains on once the alarm has finished sounding. This feature is not a necessity, but is very useful as when one returns home it will show whether or not there has been an intrusion.

## Construction

Most of the parts can be assembled on a 0.1in. pitch stripboard having 14 copper strips by 28 holes using the component lay-out shown in Fig. 9. R1 and D1 are not mounted on the panel; D1 is mounted in a panel holder somewhere on the alarm, and R1 is mounted on D1. These two components are simply wired in series across the supply lines, but make sure that the polarity of D1 is correct.

It is recommended that the speaker should not have an impedance other than 8 ohms as using a higher impedance will result in a considerable reduction in output power. A lower impedance speaker could overload the circuit.

Transistor Tr1 does not have to dissipate very much power when one takes into account it is a power transistor, but in the interest of good reliability it is a good idea to fit it with a small commercially produced vaned heatsink.

The current consumption of the unit is quite high, being a little under 1 Amp. from a 9 volt supply, and slightly in excess of 1 Amp. from a 12 volt supply (about 24 and 27mA

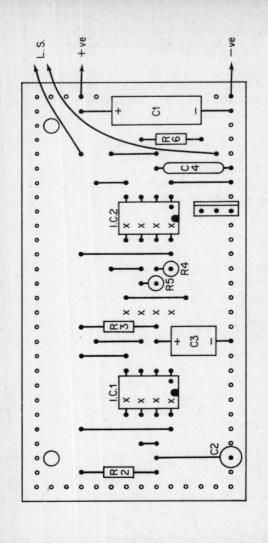

Fig. 9. A suitable stripboard layout for the circuit of Fig. 8.

respectively when the alarm switches off). This can either be supplied by a mains power supply or from high capacity batteries such as a number of HP2 cells connected in series. Small batteries such as PP3s, PP7s, etc. are not able to supply sufficient current to properly drive the circuit. Similarly, the loudspeaker must not be a miniature type as these are only able to handle about 100 to 300mV., and are not very efficient anyway. Use a large type capable of handling at least 4 watts R.M.S.

If the auto turn-off facility is not required, the following components should be omitted:— R1, R2, R3, D1, I.C.1, C2, and C3. Pin 4 of I.C.2 should then be connected to the positive supply rail.

## Components For Tone Generator With Auto Turn Off.

**Resistors.** All ¼ watt 10%.

| | | | |
|---|---|---|---|
| R1 | 680 ohms. | R4 | 33k. |
| R2 | 560k. | R5 | 33k. |
| R3 | 18k. | R6 | 180 ohms. |

**Capacitors.**

| | |
|---|---|
| C1 | 100mfd. 16v.w. |
| C2 | 470mfd. 10v.w. |
| C3 | 4.7mfd. 16v.w. |
| C4 | 10nf type C280. |

**Semiconductors.**

| | |
|---|---|
| I.C.1 | NE555V or equivalent. |
| I.C.2 | NE555V or equivalent. |
| Tr1 | TIP41A. |
| D1 | TIL 209 or similar pane L.E.D. with holder. |

**Miscellaneous.**
0.1in. matrix panel stripboard panel.
8 ohm impedance loudspeaker (see text).
Case, connecting wire, solder, etc.

## Modulated Tone Generator

As mentioned earlier, audible alarms are often made intermittent or the tone is modulated in some way so as to make
the signal more noticeable and less easily masked by other
sounds. It is an easy matter to convert the circuit of Fig. 8
to provide a frequency modulated tone, and the necessary
additional circuitry is shown in Fig. 10.

This consists of a second NE555V astable multivibrator
circuit, but the component values produce an operating
frequency of only about 5Hz. The output of this circuit is
connected to pin 5 of the tone generator I.C. (I.C.2) via R9.

Pin 5 of an NE555V timer connects to an internal potential
divider circuit which produces an output equal to two thirds
of the supply rail voltage. It is this potential divider which
sets the level at which the timing capacitor begins to discharge.

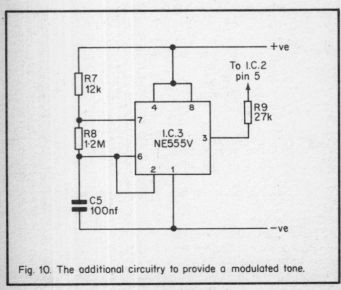

Fig. 10. The additional circuitry to provide a modulated tone.

By using an external resistor to shunt one or other of the internal resistors in the potential divider chain it is possible to raise or lower the level at which the timing capacitor begins to discharge. If this voltage is raised, it must take the timing capacitor longer to achieve the discharge threshold voltage, and the frequency of oscillation is consequently reduced. If the voltage is reduced, then the discharge threshold voltage will be produced across the timing capacitor much more quickly, and the frequency of oscillation will be increased. Thus it is possible to frequency modulate the tone by applying a modulating signal to pin 5 of the tone generator I.C.

Therefore, when the output of I.C.3 is high, the frequency of the tone will be lower than its nominal level, and when I.C.3 output is low, the tone will be higher than its nominal frequency. In this way I.C.3 rapidly switches the tone between two frequencies, neither of which are the normal operating frequency of the tone generator.

The difference in the frequency of the two tones can be increased or decreased by reducing or increasing the value of R9, if desired. Also, the rate at which the tone is switched from one frequency to the other can be altered by changing the value of C5, if this should be thought necessary.

### Construction

The size of the stripboard panel must be increased to 39 holes by 14 copper strips in order to accommodate the modulator circuitry. The right hand side of the board is wired up in the same manner as shown in Fig. 9, and the modulator circuitry is constructed on the left hand portion of the board using the component layout illustrated in Fig. 11. Construction of the unit is the same in other respects. Although the alarms described in this Chapter have been put forward for use in the home, they are also suitable for use in cars, boats, outbuildings, etc., where the requirements of a burglar alarm are much the same.

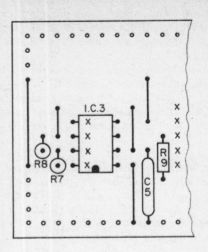

Fig. 11. The stripboard layout for the circuit of Fig. 10.

## Additional Components For Modulated Tone.

**Resistors.**

| R7 | 12k. |
|----|------|
| R8 | 1.2 Meg. |
| R9 | 27k. |

**Capacitor.**

C5          100nf type C280.

**Semiconductor.**

I.C.3          NE555V or equivalent.

36

# CHAPTER 2

## Other Types Of Burglar Alarm

There are more sophisticated ways of detecting an intruder than using switch type detectors, and this Chapter will provide details of a few devices in this type, including infra-red and ultrasonic systems. A simple burglar deterrent is also described.

### Infra-Red Beam

Probably most readers are familiar with broken beam alarm systems. In use, a beam of light is aimed at the light sensor so that the relay is not normally activated. However, if someone should come between the light source and the detector the light will be blocked from the sensor and the alarm will be activated, and since light is visible, it is quite possible that the intruder would see the beam and avoid it. In fact, in an unlit room at night it would be difficult for an intruder not to spot the beam.

A better form of broken light beam alarm is one which employs infra-red light. Infra-red occurs in the light spectrum at frequencies just below the lower limit to which the human eye is sensitive, and it cannot therefore be seen. Infra-red is often referred to as heat energy rather than light energy.

The advantage of infra-red in this application is obvious; the beam is invisible, even in the dark, so the installation is unlikely to be spotted by an intruder. The disadvantage of this system is that the circuitry and the set-up in general tends to be more complicated and expensive. However, the increase in cost and complexity is fully justified by the increased security such a system provides.

The problem with infra-red systems is that it is difficult to produce a reliable circuit with good range using d.c. circuitry.

By utilizing readily available components it is difficult to produce an infra-red beam of reasonable intensity. This produces difficulties with detecting the small d.c. change which occurs at the photosensitive detector when the beam is broken, and using it to provide a reliable switching action.

This can be overcome by modulating the infra-red beam with an audio tone, so that a small audio frequency signal is produced at the detector. It is then an easy matter to amplify this, smooth it and rectify it, and thus produce a strong d.c. signal which can be used to operate a simple relay driver circuit. Capacitive coupling can then be used in the amplifying stages and the d.c. stability of these circuits then becomes of minor importance. Good reliability is thus obtained.

An advantage of this method is that if the installation should be seen by the intruder, and he should attempt to defeat it by shining a torch at the detector as he passes through the beam, this will not be effective. A torch will provide a reasonably high infra-red output, but as the beam is not modulated it will not produce the audio signal at the detector which is needed in order to generate the d.c. bias which holds the relay circuit in the "off" state. Therefore, unlike a d.c. system, a torch cannot be used to defeat a modulated beam system.

### Transmitter

The circuit diagram of the transmitter appears in Fig. 12. This is extremely simple and merely consists of an NE555V timer I.C. connected in the astable mode. The circuit oscillates at approximately 450Hz, but the actual modulation frequency is not at all critical.

The output of the NE555V is used to drive an ordinary torch bulb. It has already been pointed out that a torch produces a reasonable amount of infra-red, and so this is an obvious choice for the basis of the unit. In order to obtain a reasonable range it is necessary for the infra-red light to be gathered and aimed at the receiver, and this can be accomplished using the reflector assembly from a torch.

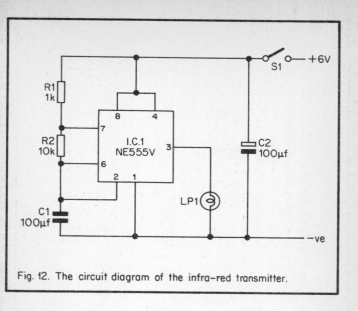

Fig. 12. The circuit diagram of the infra-red transmitter.

The prototype is based on the reflector assembly removed from an Ever Ready torch of the type which takes a 1289 4.5 volt flat battery, and this is fitted with a 3.5 volt 0.3 Amp. bulb. One output lead from the transmitter is soldered direct to the connection at the rear of the bulb and the other is soldered to the piece of metal at the front of the on/off switch (the latter then being inoperative and simply ignored).

Obviously the visible light output of the torch must be filtered out if a proper invisible, infra-red only, beam is to be produced. This can be achieved by using a Kodak 87C or 88A infra-red filter over the front of the torch reflector assembly. Any similar filter should also be suitable. Filters of this type can be obtained from some of the larger photographic stockists.

A suitable 0.1in. matrix stripboard layout for the infra-red transmitter is provided in Fig. 13. Construction of this is quite straightforward.

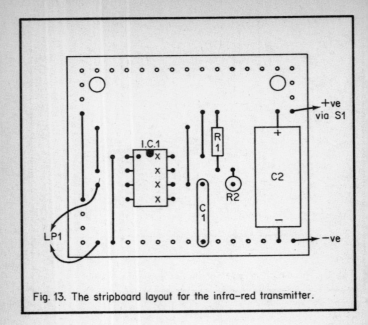

Fig. 13. The stripboard layout for the infra-red transmitter.

The circuit can be supplied from a 4.5 volt battery or a stabilised mains power supply having an output voltage of about 4.5 to 5 volts. The average current consumption of the device is a little under 150mA., and not about 300mA., as the bulb rating would suggest. This is due to a limited extent to losses in I.C.1, but is mainly because the beam is modulated, and the bulb is not supplied with power for about 50% of the time. As the current consumption of the unit is fairly high, battery operation would be rather uneconomic unless a rechargeable type such as NiCad cells are used.

**Components For Infra-Red Transmitter.**

**Resistors.** Both ¼ watt 10%.
R1          1k.
R2          10k.

40

**Capacitors.**
C1          100nf type C280.
C2          100mfd. 10v.w.

**Semiconductor.**
I.C.1        NE555V or equivalent.

**Switch.**
S1          S.P.S.T. toggle switch.

**Miscellaneous.**
0.1in. matrix stripboard panel.
Bulb, reflector assembley from torch, and I.R. filter(see text).
Case,connecting wire , solder, etc.


# Receiver

The circuit diagram of the receiver is shown in Fig. 14.
D4 is an infra-red detector diode which is used here as infra-red "battery" rather than the more usual photoconductive cell arrangement. Each time D4 receives a pulse of infra-red light it produces a small output voltage pulse, and these are considerably amplified by two common emitter amplifiers which are based on Tr1 and Tr2. These amplifiers are quite straightforward except for C4, which is needed in order to provide high frequency roll off and help to maintain the stability of the circuit.

The strong output pulses from Tr2 collector are fed to a simple rectifier and smoothing circuit which uses C5, D1, D2, and C7. The positive d.c. output from these is used to bias Tr3 on, and prevent I.C.1 from being switched on by clamping its CK terminal to the negative supply rail.

In the absence of any pulses from D4 the bias needed to hold Tr3 on quickly dies away, and I.C.1 is switched on by the small bias current which flows into its GK terminal via R6 and R7. This results in power being applied to the relay coil as this forms the load for I.C.1. Once switched on, I.C.1

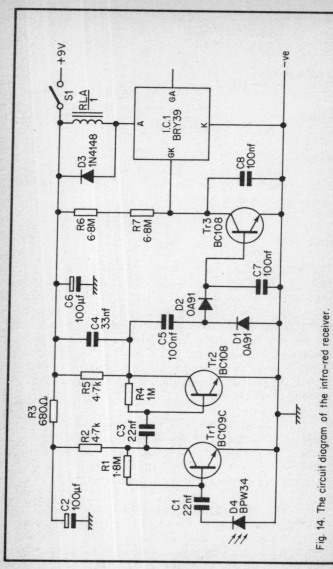

Fig. 14. The circuit diagram of the infra-red receiver.

42

latches in that state, and the relay will remain on even if the infra-red beam is restored and D4 starts to produce a signal once more.

D3 is the usual protective diode which suppresses the high back e.m.f. which would otherwise be produced across the relay coil when it de-energised. C8 momentarily holds the GK terminal of I.C.1 at the negative supply rail potential when the circuit is first switched on, and this is necessary as I.C.1 would otherwise switch on immediately S1 was closed, before enough voltage to switch on Tr3 could be developed across C7.

## Construction

The infra-red receiver can be constructed on a 0.1in. pitch stripboard panel having 15 copper strips by 33 holes using the component layout shown in Fig. 15. The polarity of D4 is not indicated in the diagram as in this particular application it is unimportant. When soldering D1 and D2 into circuit it should be remembered that these are germanium diodes, and can easily be damaged by excessive heat from the soldering iron.

A cut out must be made in the case to allow the infra-red beam to reach D4, and the component panel must be mounted in a position which brings the infra-red sensitive surface of D4 in line behind the cut out. The sensitive surface of D4, incidentally, is the dark blue area which is approximately 3 mm. square.

The quiescent current consumption of the unit is quite low at a little under 2mA., and this rises to something in the region of 30mA when the relay is activated (the precise figure depending upon the coil resiatance of the relay used).

It should be possible to obtain a maximum range of about 2 metres from the equipment, but the range of the unit is largely dependent on the properties of the particular reflector

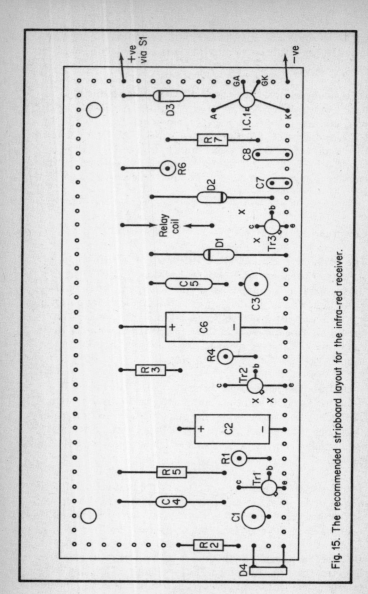

Fig. 15. The recommended stripboard layout for the infra-red receiver.

44

used, and to a more limited extent on the particular components employed in the unit. A reflector which provides a narrow
central beam will produce a greater maximum range than one
having a wide main beam. In most cases a range of about 2
metres will be sufficient as systems of this type are often set
up across a doorway or a corridor where a somewhat limited
range is all that is required.

It is possible to considerably increase the maximum range
of the equipment, if necessary, by adding a plano convex or
double convex lens in front of the infra-red detector diode
(D4). The diode is positioned in line behind the lens, and the
distance between the diode and the lens should be equal to
the focal distance of the lens. The effect of the lens is to
gather up the infra-red radiation received over its fairly large
surface area, and concentrate this onto the comparatively
small surface area of D4, as shown in Fig. 16.

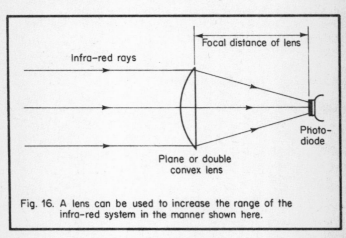

Fig. 16. A lens can be used to increase the range of the
infra-red system in the manner shown here.

The exact characteristics of the lens are not too important:
any type having a diameter of about 20mm. to 50mm. or
so and a focal length in the region of 50 to 100mm. should be
suitable. Concave lenses are totally unsuitable for this application though. A small to medium size magnifying glass lens
should do if nothing better can be obtained.

If the focal length of the lens is not known, the best position for the diode can be located by standing a few feet in front of the lens, and holding the diode in place behind the lens. With the diode right up to the lens the degree of magnification will be extremely small. As the lens is drawn back from the lens it will produce an increasingly large image which will eventually occupy the whole lens. It is the correct distance from the lens when it is drawn just far enough away from the lens to achieve this.

There is no need to use an infra-red filter in front of D4 as this component has an integral filter. For this reason, and because a modulated beam is used, the system is not affected much by the ambient lighting conditions. However, electric lighting driven from the mains will produce a certain amount of 50Hz (the mains frequency) modulated infra-red, and could conceivably hold the circuit in the off position even if the beam were to be broken. Thus it is advisable to position the receiver where it will not be subjected to strong mains lighting, or make sure that D4 is shielded from any such lighting.

**Components For Infra-Red Receiver.**

**Resistors**. All ¼ watt 10%.

| | |
|---|---|
| R1 | 1.8 Meg. |
| R2 | 4.7k. |
| R3 | 680 ohms. |
| R4 | 1 Meg. |
| R5 | 4.7k. |
| R6 | 6.8 Meg. |
| R7 | 6.8 Meg. |

**Capacitors.**

| | |
|---|---|
| C1 | 22nf type C281. |
| C2 | 100mfd. 10v.w. |
| C3 | 22nf type C281. |
| C4 | 33nf type C280. |
| C5 | 100nf type C280. |
| C6 | 100mfd. 10v.w. |

| C7 | 100nf type C280. |
| C8 | 100nf type C280. |

**Semiconductors.**

| I.C.1 | BRY39. |
| Tr1 | BC109C. |
| Tr2 | BC108. |
| Tr3 | BC108. |
| D1 | OA91. |
| D2 | OA91. |
| D3 | 1N4148. |
| D4 | BPW34 (Electrovalue or A. Marshall). |

**Switch.**

| S1 | S.P.S.T. key switch. |

**Relay.**

Nominal 6 volt operation, coil resistance about 185 ohms or more, and sufficient contacts of the appropriate type and rating for the load(s) employed.

**Miscellaneous.**

0.1in. pitch stripboard panel.
Case, connecting wire, solder, etc.
Convex lens if necessary (see text).

**Ultrasonic Beam**

There are other types of broken beam alarm apart from those which utilize some form of light, and an ultrasonic beam alarm is one of the most simple but effective of the devices which fall into this category. An ultrasonic beam is simply a stream of highly directional high frequency sound waves. A sound beam obviously cannot be seen by an intruder, and as the frequency of the beam is well above the upper frequency limit of human hearing, either can it be heard by an intruder. Therefore, like an infra-red beam, there is little chance of a burglar detecting the installation and simply avoiding the beam.

## Transmitter

An ultrasonic transmitter for use in a broken beam alarm system is extremely simple, and consists of an oscillator circuit which feeds a special ultrasonic transducer. The circuit diagram of such a transmitter is given in Fig. 17. This is based on a CMOS 4047 device which can be used in a variety of astable and monostable multivibrator modes. In this case it is wired as a straight forward free running astable circuit.

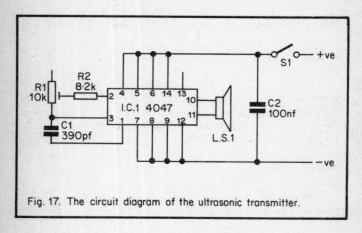

Fig. 17. The circuit diagram of the ultrasonic transmitter.

L.S.1 is not an ordinary moving coil loudspeaker, and these are not really suitable as they do not function efficiently at ultrasonic frequencies. This is a special type of transducer which uses the piezoelectric principle and is therefore more like a crystal earpiece than a moving coil loudspeaker.

At most frequencies the ultrasonic transducer is not very efficient, but at its resonant frequency (which is usually 40kHz nominal) the efficiency reaches a sudden and pronounced peak.

The transmitter must be tuned to this frequency in order to obtain good results, and in this case the transmitter can be set to the appropriate frequency by adjusting preset resistor R1.

C2 is simply a supply decoupling capacitor and S1 is an ordinary on/off switch.

Some readers may be puzzled by the fact that neither of the connections to L.S.1 is an earth connection. The transducer is actually driven from the Q and $\overline{Q}$ (or not Q) outputs of the 4047 astable. When the Q output is low, the $\overline{Q}$ one is high, and vice versa. Thus the transducer first has one connection low and the other one high, then the low connection goes high and the high one becomes low, and so on as the outputs switch from one state to the other.

This results in the peak to peak voltage produced across the transducer being almost equal to double the supply rail potential, since it is first subjected to a positive voltage virtually equal to the supply potential, then a negative voltage almost equal to the supply potential and so on. The peak to peak signal amplitude across the transducer would only be about half this level if the device was to be connected between the negative supply rail and one of the outputs. This would result in a weaker signal from the transmitter with consequent reduced maximum range.

### Receiver Circuit

This appears in Fig. 18 and is a little more complicated than the transmitter circuit. The microphone is not an ordinary type, but is a special ultrasonic type, as described in the previous paragraph, and will produce a 40kHz signal when it receives the ultrasonic soundwaves from the transmitter. Like an ordinary microphone, however, the output from the device will be only quite small; perhaps only a fraction of a millivolt when the two transducers are some distance apart. In order to drive a relay from this signal it is therefore necessary to considerably amplify it.

The initial amplification is provided by Tr1 which is connected as a high gain low noise common emitter amplifier. The output from this stage is coupled to the non-inverting input of I.C.1.

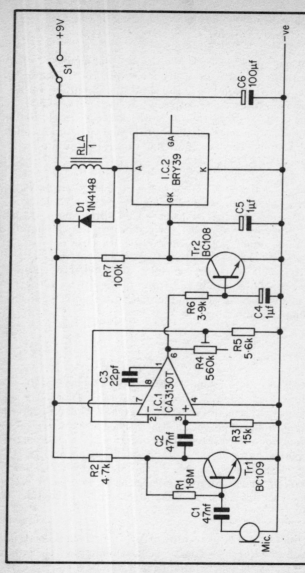

Fig. 18. The circuit diagram of the ultrasonic receiver.

This is an operational amplifier which is used here as an active rectifier. R3 is used to bias the non-inverting input of the device to earth potential and R4 plus R5 form a negative feedback loop between the output and the inverting input. Under quiescent conditions the circuit is biased so that the output is at earth potential, but positive going input half cycles will be amplified and will cause the output to swing positive to the earth rail. Negative going input half cycles will have no effect on the output since only a single supply rail is used (rather than the usual dual balanced supplies that are used with operational amplifiers), and so the output cannot swing negative to the earth rail Thus the circuit provides both amplification and rectification. C3 is the compensation capacitor for I.C.1.

Tr2 is used in the common emitter mode and has R7 as its collector load. Its base terminal is driven from the output of I.C.1 via R6 and C4. These last two components protect the base emitter junction of Tr2 against passing an excessive current and smooth the output pulses from I.C.1 to form a d.c. bias which switches on Tr2. Only a very low voltage therefore appears at Tr2 collector, and I.C.2 (which has its GK terminal fed from this point) is switched off.

If the ultrasonic beam should be broken, and the output pulses from I.C.1 should cease, the voltage across C4 will very quickly decay and Tr2 will turn off. This will cause its collector potential to rise and I.C.2 will be switched on. I.C.2 has a relay as its load, and so the relay will be switched on. Once I.C.2 has turned on it will latch in that state, and restoring the ultrasonic beam will cause the circuit to revert to its original state.

D1 is the usual protective diode and S1 is the on/off switch. C5 holds the GK terminal of I.C.2 at earth potential when the supply is first connected to the unit. This gives the voltage across C4 time to build up and switch on Tr2, and thus prevents I.C.2 from switching on the moment the supply is connected. C6 is an ordinary supply decoupling capacitor.

## Construction

The transmitter circuit is constructed on a 0.1in. pitch stripboard panel having 13 holes by 19 copper strips using the component layout which is illustrated in Fig. 19. The receiver is also constructed on a 0.1in matrix stripboard panel, but this one has 32 holes by 12 copper strips and uses the component layout shown in Fig. 20.

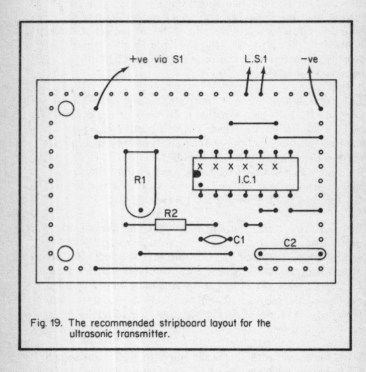

Fig. 19. The recommended stripboard layout for the
ultrasonic transmitter.

The construction of these panels is quite straightforward except that it must be borne in mind that I.C.1 of the transmitter is a CMOS device and I.C.1 of the receiver has a CMOS input stage. Observe the usual precautions when handling.

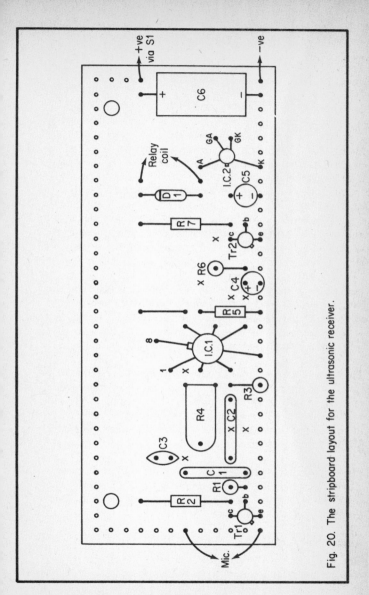

Fig. 20. The stripboard layout for the ultrasonic receiver.

53

The 4047 is not one of the cheapest CMOS I.C.s and it is probably worthwhile using an I.C. socket for this component. The CA3130T device used in the receiver must be soldered direct to the stripboard.

Ultrasonic transducers are normally sold in matched pairs (one for the transmitter and one for the receiver) and any types sold through normal retail outlets and for operation at about 40kHz should be suitable for this design. It should be noted that with some types of transducer the transmitting and receiving units are identical, but with others there are specific units for use in the transmitter and receiver. The retailer's catalogue or other literature will usually provide the relevant information if this is the case, and should be consulted. However, even if the transmitting and receiving transducers should happen to be accidentally transposed, the system will almost certainly still operate perfectly satisfactorily!

No particular make and type of transducer has been specified as these devices tend to come and go as slightly improved versions are developed. The prototype was tested using the R1400P units sold by Arrow Electronics Ltd., but virtually identical results should be obtained using any similar type.

The transducers must either be mounted on the outside of the transmitter and receiver cases, or they should be mounted behind cut outs in the cases so that there is no hindrance to the exit and access of the ultrasonic waves. Probably the easiest way of mounting the transducers is to glue them in place using a high quality adhesive such as an epoxy type.

The receiver has a quiescent current consumption of about 3mA from a 9 volt supply, but this increases to about 30mA. when the alarm is triggered. The current consumption of the transmitter is approximately 9mA.

### Adjustment And Use

One way of correctly adjusting R1 of the transmitter is to connect the receiving transducer to a millivoltmeter (A.C. type) and then place the transducer so that if receives the output from an operating ultrasonic transmitter. If R1 is adjusted for maximum meter reading it will then have the optimum setting.

An alternative method is to set the system up with the transmitter and receiver some distance apart, connect a multimeter set to read 10 volts f.s.d. between the negative supply rail (negative test prod) and pin 6 of I.C.1 in the receiver, and then adjust R1 of the transmitter for maximum meter reading.

It is also possible to find a satisfactory setting for R1 if no test equipment is availbale, but it is then simply a matter of trial and error with R1 being tried at various settings in an attempt to find one which gives good sensitivity.

R4 in the receiver will normally need to be adjusted for maximum sensitivity (set in a fully clockwise direction) but under certain circumstances the system may be found to be more reliable if it is backed off somewhat. This will increase the level of negative feedback applied to I.C.1 and will thus reduce its closed loop voltage gain.

The system should operate over a range of at least 6 metres without any difficulty, and the maximum attainable range will probably be 10 metres or so. However, in the interest of reliability it is advisable not to use the system at anything like maximum range as a fall off in performance for any reason would then result in a false alarm. 6 metres or so should therefore be regarded as the maximum usable range.

There is no need to attempt to focus the ultrasonic waves from the transmitter into a narrow beam as the transducers are inherently highly directional anyway. The only problem which might occur with system is that of the ultrasonic waves being reflected around the room and reaching the receiver by some indirect route. This could possibly result in the receiver picking up a significant signal even when the beam is broken. If this should happen, reducing the sensitivity of the receiver slightly by backing off R4 should eliminate this problem.

## Components For Ultrasonic Transmitter.

**Resistors.**
R1          10k subminiature (0.1 watt) horizontal preset.
R2          8.2k ¼ watt 10%.

**Capacitors.**
C1          390pf ceramic plate.
C2          100nf type C280.

**Semiconductor.**
I.C.1        CMOS 4047.

**Switch.**
S1          S.P.S.T. toggle switch.

**Transducer.**
L.S.1.       40kHz ultrasonic transducer (see text).

**Miscellaneous**
0.1in. matrix stripboard panel.
Cases, connecting wire, solder, etc.


## Components for Ultrasonic Receiver

**Resistors.** All ¼ watt 10%.
R1          1.8 Meg.
R2          4.7k.
R3          15k.
R4          560k subminiature (0.1 watt) horizontal preset.
R5          5.6k.
R6          3.9k.
R7          100k.

**Capacitors.**
C1          47nf type C280.
C2          47nf type C280.
C3          22pf ceramic plate.
C4          1mfd. 10v.w.

| C5 | 1mfd. 10v.w. |
| C6 | 100mfd. 10v.w. |

**Semiconductors.**

| I.C.1. | CA3130T. |
| I.C.2. | BRY39. |
| Tr1 | BC109. |
| Tr2 | BC108. |
| D1 | 1N4148. |

**Switch.**

| S1 | S.P.S.T. key switch. |

**Relay.**

Nominal 6 volt operation, coil resistance of about 185 ohms or more, and sufficient contacts of the appropriate type and rating for the load(s) employed.

**Transducer.**

40kHz ultrasonic transducer (see text).

**Miscellaneous.**

0.1in. matrix stripboard panel.
Case, connecting wire, solder, etc.

**Doppler Shift Alarm**

Probably most readers will be familiar with the term 'Doppler Shift'. This is the apparent shift in frequency which occurs when energy waves of some form are emitted by a moving object. If the object is coming towards you any waves it sends out will appear to be at a higher frequency than they actually are, and if the object is moving away from you there will be an apparent drop in frequency. This is demonstrated by a fast moving car which passes by while sounding its horn. There is a sudden and large drop in the frequency of the note from the horn as the car passes by.

This effect can be used as the basis for an ultrasonic intruder detector using the general arrangement shown in Fig.21.

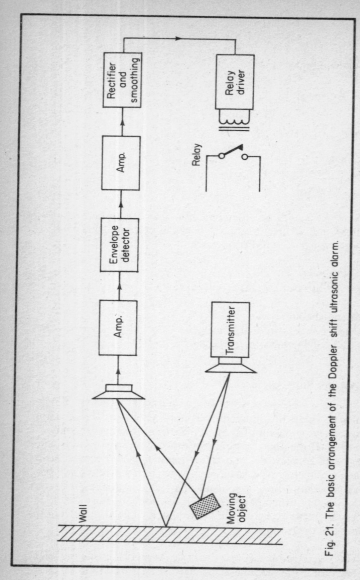

Fig. 21. The basic arrangement of the Doppler shift ultrasonic alarm.

The signal from the transmitter is directed to the receiver by indirect means, in this case by reflecting the signal off a wall. In this way it is possible for the system to cover a fairly large area, which is its main advantage over the more simple broken beam type alarm. If a moving object causes some of the transmitter to be reflected to the receiver, a shift in frequency will be produced on this signal. The receiver is designed to detect the presence of more than one input signal frequency, and operate a relay in this event.

A high gain amplifier is used at the input of the receiver, and the output from this is fed to an envelope detector (which is an ordinary a.m. type detector of the same kind that is used in a.m. radio receivers). If there is only one input signal frequency, the only output from the detector will be a d.c. bias. If, on the other hand, a moving object causes a Doppler Shift of say 50Hz in part of the signal, this will produce an audio output of 50Hz from the detector. This is caused by the main signal and the Doppler shifted signal reacting at the detector to produce a beat note, as will any two frequencies that are fed to an envelope detector.

In practice the output frequency from the envelope detector will depend upon how slow or fast the object is moving, and will normally be in the region of a few hundred Hz to as little as a few Hz.

The output from the detector is amplified and then rectified and smoothed to produce a d.c. signal. This is used to operate a latching relay driver circuit. Under quiescent conditions there will be no output from the detector and the relay will not be operated. However, virtually any moving object will produce sufficient a.c. output from the detector to operate the relay and sound the alarm.

**Receiver Circuit**

An ultrasonic transmitter for use in a Doppler Shift system is no different to that employed in a broken beam alarm system,

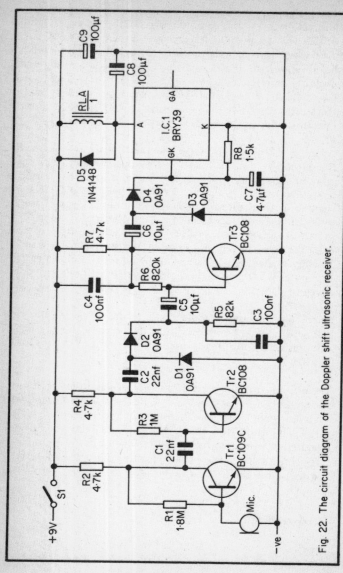

Fig. 22. The circuit diagram of the Doppler shift ultrasonic receiver.

60

and so the transmitter described earlier in this book is also suitable for use in this application. However, the receiver needs to be a little more sophisticated. The circuit diagram of such a unit appears in Fig. 22.

The microphone is coupled to the input of a straightforward high gain common emitter amplifier which utilizes Tr1. The output from this is coupled to a second common emitter amplifier which is based on Tr2. The output from this stage is fed to a simple detector circuit which uses D1, D2, C3 and R5.

C5 filters out the d.c. component produced by the detector and feeds the a.c. signal to a third common emitter stage, this one being based on Tr3. C4 is needed in order to filter out any of the ultrasonic signal which leaks through to this amplifier, and which could otherwise upset the operation of the receiver.

The output from Tr3 is fed to the rectifier and smoothing network which consists of D3, D4, and C7. Normally the GK terminal of I.C.1 is held at the negative supply rail voltage by R8, but if a Doppler Shift occurs, the positive output from the smoothing and rectifier circuit will be sufficient to take this terminal about 0.5 volts or so positive and I.C.1 will be switched on. Once switched on it will remain so, and the relay which forms its load will also be swithced on.

C8 is needed in order to prevent the circuit from triggering to the "on" state the moment the supply is connected. D5 is a protective diode and C9 is the only supply decoupling capacitor that is required. S1 is the on/off switch. The quiescent current consumption of the circuit is only about 3mA. from a 9 volt supply and this rises to about 30mA. when the relay is activated.

## Construction

A suitable 0.1in. matrix stripboard layout for the unit is provided in Fig.23, and this requires a board having 15 copper strips by 31 holes.

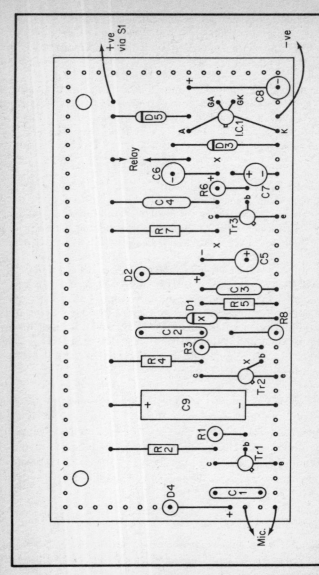

Fig. 23. The stripboard layout for the Doppler shift ultrasonic receiver.

62

The completed unit requires no adjustment, but it will be necessary to experiment with positioning and orientation of the transmitter and reciever in order to obtain the best possible coverage of the designated area. It is possible to cover an area of a few metres square, but sensitivity will not be optimum over the entire area. However, as the unit is extremely sensitive at favourable parts of the covered area, such as directly in line with one of the transducers, there is no need to achieve optimum sensitivity over the entire covered area. When in parts of the room where the system is most effective the movement of a hand or even just a finger can be sufficient to trigger the circuit!

One obvious problem with this system is that of leaving the room once the uint has been switched on. It is possible to move **around in the area covered by the** system if one moves extremely slowly, but obviously this is not a very practical method of leaving the room once the system has been switched on. A better alternative would be to construct a simple timer which would provide a delay between the unit being switched on and it coming into operation, so as to give time for the operator to make an exit. However, this would still leave the problems of re-entering the room without triggering the alarm so that the unit could be switched off.

There are some more practical approaches to the problem, such as simply situating the on/off switch outside the room in which the equipment is installed. The area to the rear of the transducers is usually largely or completely insensitive, and it is possible to make this area coincide with the entrance to the room so that there is then no problem with entering the room and switching the system off.

Note that in order to avoid accidentally triggering the system when switching it on or off, always switch on the transmitter before turning on the receiver, and switch off the receiver before turning off the transmitter.

## Components For Dopler Shift Ultrasonic Receiver.

**Resistors.** All ¼ watt 10%.

| | |
|---|---|
| R1 | 1.8 Meg. |
| R2 | 4.7k. |
| R3 | 1 Meg. |
| R4 | 4.7k. |
| R5 | 82k. |
| R6 | 820k. |
| R7 | 4.7k. |
| R8 | 1.5k. |

**Capacitors.**

| | |
|---|---|
| C1 | 22nf type C280. |
| C2 | 22nf type C280. |
| C3 | 100nf type C280. |
| C4 | 100nf type C280. |
| C5 | 10mfd. 10v.w. |
| C6 | 10mfd. 10v.w. |
| C7 | 4.7mfd. 10v.w. |
| C8 | 100mfd. 10v.w. |
| C9 | 100mfd. 10v.w. |

**Semiconductors.**

| | |
|---|---|
| I.C.1 | BRY39. |
| Tr1 | BC109C. |
| Tr2 | BC108. |
| Tr3 | BC108. |
| D1 to D4 | OA91 (4 off). |
| D5 | 1N4148. |

**Switch.**

| | |
|---|---|
| S1 | S.P.S.T. key switch. |

**Transducer.**

40kHz ultrasonic transducer.

**Relay.**

Nominal 6 volt operation, coil resistance of about 185 ohms or more, and sufficient contacts of the correct type and adequate rating for the load(s) employed.

**Miscellaneous.**
0.1in. matrix stripboard panel.
Case, connecting wire, solder, etc.


## Light Detector

A very simple sensor for an alarm system which is to operate
at night time is a light detector circuit. One way of using such
a device is to adjust it so that ambient light level in the room
is never quite strong enough to trigger the unit. However, if
an intruder should switch on the lights, or shine a torch in the
vicinity of the light sensor, this will be sufficient to trigger the
unit. This set-up relies upon the fact that the ambient light
level in the room will not be very high, but during the hours
of darkness, or in the first few hours of daylight with the
curtains in the room closed, this should be the case.

It is also possible to use a light sensor in a system which will
operate during the day or at night. For example, the sensor
can be fitted in a cupboard which contains some valuables.
Normally the inside of the cupboard will be in virtually total
darkness and the circuit will not be triggered, but it anyone
should open the cupboard door while the unit is switched on,
a higher level of light will reach the unit and it will activate the
the alarm. Thus such a unit can be used as a good alternative
to mirco-switches or reed switches in such applications.


## The Circuit

The circuit diagram of a very simple sensitive light detector
unit is given in Fig.24. Under dark conditions the ORP12
cadmium sulphide photoresistor used in the PCC1 position will
have a high resistance, perhaps 10 Meg. ohms or more. A potential divider circuit is formed by PCC1 plus R1, and R2. With
PCC1 in darkness only a fraction of a volt will appear at the
juntion of R1 and R2. This voltage is fed to the GK terminal

of I.C.1, and obviously falls short of the 0.5 volts of so required in order to switch this device into the "on" state. Thus in darkness the circuit will not be triggered.

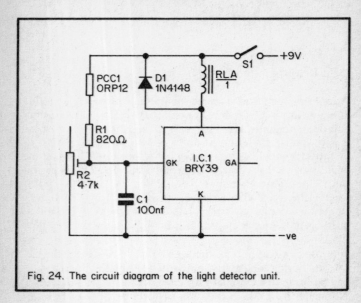

Fig. 24. The circuit diagram of the light detector unit.

When subjected to moderately light conditions, the resistance of PCC1 falls considerably, probably to a few tens of k ohms or less, and under very bright conditions its resistance will fall to only a few tens of ohms. In either case the voltage at the GK terminal of I.C.1 will rise to a high enough level to turn the device on and activate the relay coil which forms its load. Once triggered, I.C.1 will remain on even if PCC1 is returned to dark conditions. The only way to de-energise the relay is to remove the power from the circuit using S1. This also causes the current through I.C.1 to fall to a very low level so that I.C.1 switches off, and is ready to commence operation once again when the supply is restored.

Adjusting R2 will raise or lower the minimum resistance needed by PCC1 to trigger the circuit, and in this way the sensitivity of the circuit can be varied over very wide limits.

C1 is needed in order to ensure that spurious triggering of the circuit does not occur and D1 is a protective diode. S1 is the on/off switch, and if the circuit is housed along with the rest of the alarm circuitry, S1 can be the on/off switch for the entire system. PCC1 would then probably need to be mounted remotely from the rest of the unit, but this is quite acceptable and the two way connecting cable can be several metres long if necessary.

The unit can be constructed on a 0.1in. matrix stripboard panel using the component layout illustrated in Fig.25. The panel has 11 copper strips by 13 holes and there are no breaks in any of the copper strips. Construction of this very simple circuit is quite straightforward and should present no problems even to a beginner.

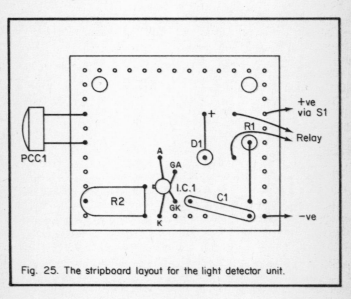

Fig. 25. The stripboard layout for the light detector unit.

## Components For Light Detector.

**Resistors.**

| | |
|---|---|
| R1 | 820 ohms ¼ watt 10%. |
| R2 | 4.7k subminiature (0.1 watt) horizontal preset. |
| PCC1 | ORP12. |

**Capacitor.**

| | |
|---|---|
| C1 | 100nf type C280. |

**Semiconductors.**

| | |
|---|---|
| I.C.1 | BRY39. |
| D1 | 1N4148. |

**Switch.**

| | |
|---|---|
| S1 | S.P.S.T. key switch. |

**Relay.**
Nominal 6 volt operation, coil resistance of about 185 ohms or more, and sufficient contacts of correct type and adequate rating for the load(s) employed.

**Miscellaneous.**
0.1in. pitch stripboard panel.
Wire, solder, etc.

## Automatic Light

This very simple device is intended to act as a deterrent to would-be intruders. It merely consists of a circuit which will turn a light on at dusk and switch it off again at dawn, thus giving the impression that the house is occupied even if it is not. Burglars are less likely to attack premises which appear to be occupied than premises which are believed to be empty, and in this way such a circuit provides a s imple deterrent.

The complete circuit diagram of the unit is shown in Fig.26, and as will be apparent from this, the circuit uses only five components plus the controlled lamp.

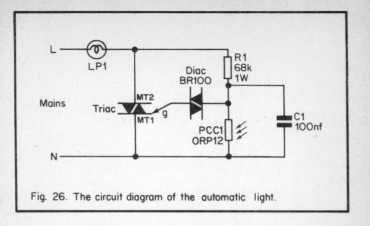

Fig. 26. The circuit diagram of the automatic light.

When the photocell is in darkness it will have a very high resistance and will not have any significant effect on the circuit.

Therefore, at the beginning of each mains half cycle C1 will rapidly charge via R1 to the trigger voltage of the diac. Once this voltage has beend reached, the previously very high impedance of the diac will fall to a very low level, and C1 will discharge through the diac into the gate circuit of the triac. This triggers the triac on, and it connects the mains supply to the load, which is the controlled light bulb of course.

When the triac turns on, the voltage across it falls to only about 1 volt, and this effectively cuts R1, C1, PCC1 and the diac out of circuit until the end of the half cycle. The current through the triac then falls to a low level and causes it to turn off. The circuit is then ready to start from the beginning when the next half cycle commences.

In this way power is supplied to the bulb when the photocell is in fairly dark conditions. Admittedly, the very beginning of each half cycle is cut out as the triac cannot fire until the voltage across C1 has reached the trigger level of the diac, but the power lost here is extremely small and is not noticable in practice.

When the photocell is subjected to fairly bright conditions
it will have a resistance of only a very few k ohms or less. A
potential divider action across R1 and PCC1 will prevent the
voltage across C1 from reaching the trigger potential of the
diac, and so the triac will not be triggered into conduction.
Therefore, when the photocell is in bright conditions the lamp
will be switched off.

## Construction

Probably the best housing for the unit is a double size wall
mounting switch box. This should have a mains socket
mounted on one side, and a blanking plate over the other
compartment. The 'Live' and 'Earth' leads of the mains cable
connect to the respective terminals of the mains socket. An
entrance hole for the mains lead should be drilled in the side
of the box adjacent to the mains socket, and this hole should
be fitted with a grommet.

A hole about 7 to 8 m.m. in diameter is drilled in the centre
of the blanking plate, and the photocell is glued in position
behind this using a powerful adhesive such as an epoxy type.
Be careful not to use an excess of adhesive so that light is
prevented from reaching the sensitive surface of the photocell
(the one opposite the leadout wires).

The remaining circuitry is assembled on a 0.15in., pitch stripboard having 8 copper strips by 8 holes, and the component
layout of this panel is given in Fig. 27. The photocell connects
to the panel via a short two way insulated lead.

The complete component panel is mounted on the base of the
case using a couple of nylon 6BA nuts and bolts. Metal mounting bolts can only be used if they are earthed, and, in fact, no
metal work should be left exposed unless it is earthed, except
for the mounting bolts for the blanking plate and mains
socket. Neither should any of the wiring be touched while the
unit is plugged into the mains as this could easily result in a
severe electric shock being obtained.

In use a standard or table lamp is plugged into the mains socket on the unit, and the unit itself is placed in a position where the photocell will receive the light from outside. It must be placed reasonably well away from the lamp so that the photocell does not receive a great deal of light from the lamp. Otherwise the unit may fail to work and could even continuously flash the lamp on and off due to positive feedback between the lamp and the photocell!

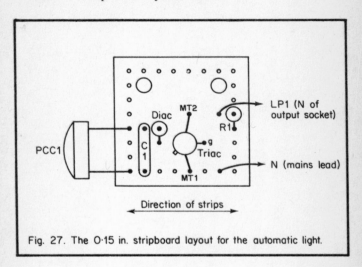

Fig. 27. The 0·15 in. stripboard layout for the automatic light.

**Components For Automatic Light.**

**Resistors.**

| | |
|---|---|
| R1 | 68k 1 watt 10%. |
| PCC1 | ORP12. |

**Capacitor.**

| | |
|---|---|
| C1 | 100nf type C280. |

**Semiconductors.**

| | |
|---|---|
| Triac | 400 volts 2 Amp. in TO5 or TO39 encapsulation. |
| Diac | BR100 or similar. |

**Miscellaneous.**
0.15in. Matrix stripboard panel.
Parts for case (see text).
Wire, solder, etc.

# CHAPTER 3

## Other Types Of Alarm

As was pointed out at the beginning of this book, not only burglar alarms are pertinent to the title 'Electronic Security Devices', and this final Chapter will deal with a few alarm circuits which fall within the security device category, but are not burglar alarms as such.

### Smoke/Gas Detector

Smoke and gas detectors are widely used in boating where bottled gas is often used to power cookers and, occasionally other pieces of equipment, such as refrigerators and heaters. Even a small gas leak can, over a period of time, cause an explosive concentration of gas to build up in the bilges, and then only a small spark (from an engine say) is all that is required to produce disastrous consequences.

Smoke and gas detectors can also be of value in the home and elsewhere, by providing an early warning of fire or a dangerous gas leak.

The unit described here employs a sensitive semiconductor gas sensor which will detect methane, propane, carbon monoxide smoke, methylated spirit vapour, etc. It will detect these gases at concentrations well below the explosive limit.

### The Circuit

The circuit diagram of the gas and smoke detector unit appears in Fig. 28. This is based on the Figaro type 812 gas sensor and this consists of a semiconductor sensor and a heating element. Under normal circumstances the semiconductor material is oxidised with oxygen in the air when it is heated,

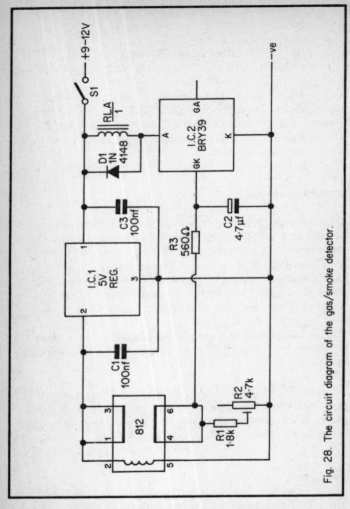

Fig. 28. The circuit diagram of the gas/smoke detector.

and will offer a very high resistance (about 100k). However, combustible gases will have a de-oxidising affect on the semi-conductor material and will cause its resistance to fall to a very low level. The circuit operates by detecting this fall in resistance.

74

The heater of the 812 gas sensor requires a supply of 5 volts and a current of about 100mA. or so, and this is derived from a small 5 volt regulator I.C. (I.C.1). This provides a well regulated supply as well as having output current limiting and thermal overload protection circuitry. C1 and C3 help to maintain the stability of the regulator I.C.

The semiconductor sensing element of the gas sensor forms one arm of a potential divider connected across the stabilised supply lines, and R1 plus R2 form the other section of this circuit. The voltage produced by this network is coupled to the GK terminal of I.C.2 via R3. R2 is adjusted so that under normal conditions there is just insufficient voltage produced by the potential divider to switch on I.C.2.

If the gas sensor should be subjected to some combustible gas, its resistance will considerably decrease and the voltage fed to the GK terminal of I.C.2 will be high enough to switch the device on. In fact, R3 must be included in the circuit to protect I.C.2 against passing an excessive gate current. A relay forms the load for I.C.2 and will be activated when gas is detected. D1 protects the circuit against the high reverse voltage which would otherwise be generated across the relay coil as it de-energised. The relay will not de-energise until the unit is switched off using S1 as once triggered the S.C.S. used in the I.C.2 position will latch in the "on" state.

If preferred, the relay can be replaced with a buzzer or a small oscillator circuit driving a loudspeaker, but the load current should not be more than about 100mA.

C2 is needed in order to prevent spurious triggering of the device. Note that the potential divider circuit must be fed from the stabilised supply line so that the voltage fed to the GK terminal of I.C.2 is not significantly affected by variations in supply potential, which could otherwise impair reliability.

## Construction

A suitable 0.1in. matrix stripboard layout for the unit is provided in Fig. 29. This requires a panel having 13 holes by 18 copper strips, and construction of the component panel should present no problems. There are no breaks in any of the copper strips, incidentally.

The 812 gas sensor has a 6 pin base which will fit into a special holder for the device, or a standard minature (B7G) seven pin valve holder can be used if preferred. The pins of the 812 device are arranged in two groups of three, as shown in Fig. 29. Note

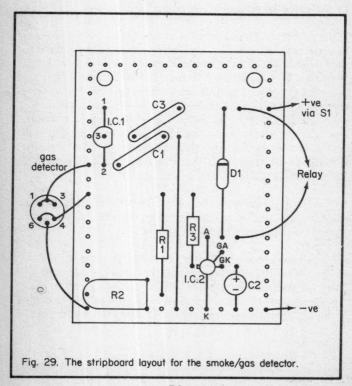

Fig. 29. The stripboard layout for the smoke/gas detector.

however, that this device is symmetrical, and it does not matter which set of pins is designated 1 to 3 or 4 to 6, and that the device can be plugged into its holder either way round.

If necessary, the gas sensor can be remotely located from the rest of the unit, and it will then be necessary to use a three way cable a few metres long between the main unit and the socket for the 812 sensor.

If R2 is adjusted in a fully anticlockwise direction, the unit should be found to work quite well. Adjusting R2 in a clockwise direction will slightly increase the sensitivity of the unit, but if it is adjusted too far it will be found that the unit is triggered soon after switch on, even if no combustible gas is present near the sensor.

The reason for this is that when power is applied to the circuit the resistance of the semiconductor material in the 812 falls slightly and then rises to its normal operating level. If R2 is adjusted too far, this dip in resistance will be sufficient to trigger the unit.

Therefore, R2 must be adjusted for a compromise between optimum sensitivity, and an absence of spurious triggering soon after switch on. Since the setting of R2 does not have a very large affect on sensitivity, it is probably better to adopt a setting which ensures good reliability, rather than attempt to obtain the absolute maximum of sensitivity.

The quiescent current consumption of the unit is a little in excess of 100mA., and this rises by about 30mA. or so when the relay is activated. The 812 gas detector has a continuous working life of about 2 years, after which it will become sluggish in operation, and must be replaced.


**Components For Gas/Smoke Detector.**

**Resistors.**
R1          1.8k ¼ watt 10%.                                    ○

| R2 | 4.7k subminiature (0.1 watt) horizontal preset. |
|---|---|
| R3 | 560 ohms ¼ watt 10%. |

**Capacitors**.

| C1 | 100nf type C280. |
|---|---|
| C2 | 4.7mfd. 10v.w. |
| C3 | 100nf type C280. |

**Semiconductors**.

| I.C.1 | $\mu$A78LO5WC, or similar 5 volt 100mA. voltage regulator. |
|---|---|
| I.C.2 | BRY39. |
| D1 | 1N4148. |
| Gas Detector | Figaro type 812 (Watford Electronics). |

**Switch**

| S1 | S.P.S.T. toggle switch. |
|---|---|

**Miscellaneous**

0.1in. matrix stripboard panel.
Holder for gas detector.
Relay for nominal 6 volt operation, coil resistance of about
185 ohms or more, and sufficient contacts for the appropriate
type and rating for the load(s) employed.
Case.
Wire, solder, etc.

**Water Activated Alarm**

Water activated switches are most frequently put forward as
rain alarms, but they have other uses in and around the home.
They can, for example, be used as flood alarms in premises
that are prone to flooding in the basement or cellar, or they
can be used to monitor the overflow pipe of cisterns which
have a habit of overflowing. There are other possible domestic
uses, and they can also be used in applications outside the
home environment, such as in boating for instance.

Units of this type rely on the fact that although the water is an insulator when it has a high degree of purity, water that will be encountered in practical applications will contain significant amounts of dissolved impurities, and will have quite a low resistance. Thus a simple water sensor can simply consist of two pieces of bare metal which are closely spaced and insulated from on another. In the absence of any water there will be an extremely high resistance between the two pieces of metal, but if they are bridged by water this resistance will fall to quite a low level. A water activated alarm merely has to sound an audible alarm when this fall in resistance is detected.

### The Circuit

Fig. 30 shows the complete circuit diagram of the water activated alarm. When there is no water on the senor, I.C.1 will have its GK terminal connected to earth via R2, and so will be switched off. Therefore no current will be fed to the load for I.C.1 which is a simple audio tone generator. The latter is based on I.C.2, and this is an NE555V timer I.C. which is used here in the astable mode. The values of R4, R3, and C3 have been chosen to produce an operating frequency of approximately 1kHz, and the roughly squarewave output from I.C.2 is used to drive loudspeaker L.S.1.

If the sensor should be bridged by some water, then a current will be fed from the positive supply rail to the GK terminal of I.C.1 via R1 and the sensor. This will cause I.C.1 to switch on, and power will be supplied to the tone generator circuit and an alarm signal will be emitted from the speaker.

S1 is the on/off switch and C1 is a supply decoupling capacitor. R1 is a current limiting resistor and is needed in order to protect I.C.1 against passing an excessive gate current.

### Construction

All the small components can be assembled on a 0.1in. pitch

stripboard panel having 14 copper strips by 16 holes using the component layout shown in Fig. 31. This is quite straightforward, but be careful not to omit any of the four breaks in

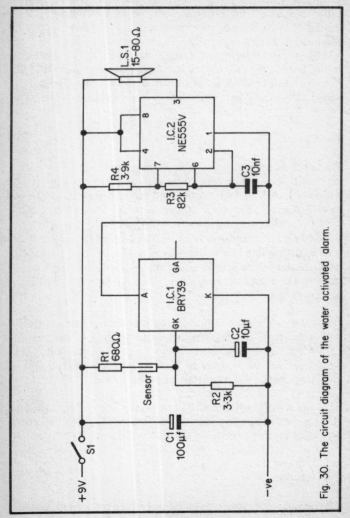

Fig. 30. The circuit diagram of the water activated alarm.

the copper strips or any of the five link wires.

With a little ingenuity it should not be too difficult to fabricate a suitable sensor for the unit. The best form for this to take will depend to a large extent on precisely how the unit is to be used, and a little common sense should be exercised here.

The quiescent current consumption of the unit is only the leakage current which flows through C1 and I.C.1, which should be no more than about 1 micro-amp. The circuit is therefore suitable for battery operation despite the fact that the unit will probably need to be left switched on for very long periods.

Even with continuous use the batteries will last for their shelf life (which should be several months).

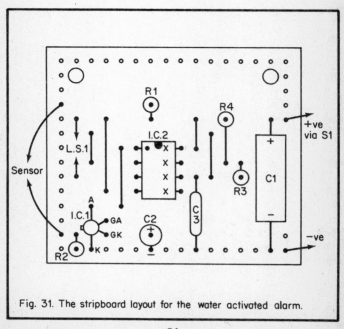

Fig. 31. The stripboard layout for the water activated alarm.

The current consumption when the alarm sounds depends upon the speaker impedance used. With an 8 ohm speaker the consumption will be a little under 50mA., but this rises to something approaching 200mA. When a 15 ohm speaker is used. If the highest possible volume is required from the unit a 15 ohm impedance speaker should be used, and larger speakers generally have higher efficiencies than miniature ones. A speaker having an impedance of less than 15 ohms must not be employed with this circuit.

## Components for Water Activated Alarm

**Resistors.** All ¼ watt 10%.
R1          680 ohms.
R2          3.3k.
R3          3.9k
R4          82k.

**Capacitors.**
C1          100mfd. 10v.w.
C2          10mfd. 10v.w.
C3          10nf. type C280.

**Semiconductors.**
I.C.1          BRY39.
I.C.2          NE555V.

**Switch.**
S1          S.P.S.T. toggle switch.

**Miscellaneous.**
0.1in. pitch stripboard panel.
15 to 80 ohm impedance loudspeaker.
Materials for sensor.
Case, connecting wire, solder, etc.

## Temperature Alarms

There are two basic types of temperature alarm: the high or over-temperature alarm and the low or under-temperature type. The former sounds an alarm of some kind when a sensor detects that the monitored temperature has gone above a certain predetermined level, and the latter is triggered when the monitorel temperature goes below a certain threshold level.

Temperature alarms can be used in a number of applications. They can be used in greenhouses to give warning if the heating system has failed or is proving to be inadequate in very adverse conditions. It is also possible for the temperature in a greenhouse to rise to unacceptably high levels in very sunny conditions and if the ventilation is inadequate. Obviously a high temperature alarm could be used to give warning of this. By using both under-temperature and over-temperature alarms it is possible to obtain an indication if the temperature should stray outside the prescribed limits.

Another use for an over-temperature alarm is as a freezer temperature monitor. Here the circuit is adjusted so that it will be triggered if the temperature in the freezer rises more than marginally above its normal operating level. It thus gives warning if the apparatus should fail for any reason, and gives sufficient time for remedial action to be taken before the contents of the freezer become spoilt.

Temperature alarms are also used in ice warning devices for cars, simple fire alarm systems, and there must be many other possible uses for these devices.

## High Temperature Alarm

The circuit diagram of a simple over-temperature alarm is shown in Fig. 32. This is based on operational amplifier I.C.2, but this device is used here as a comparator.

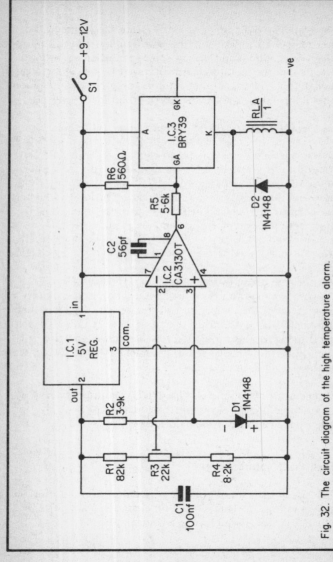

Fig. 32. The circuit diagram of the high temperature alarm.

The non-inverting (+) input of I.C.2 is fed from a silicon diode (D1) which is forward biased by R2. When connected in this fashion a silicon diode will operate as a sort of Zener diode and a stabilised voltage of about 0.65 volts will be produced. However, the precise voltage developed across the diode will be affected to some extent by the junction temperature of the device, and will vary by about 2 to three millivolts per degree Centigrade change in temperature. A silicon diode has a negative temperature coefficient (ie. a rise in temperature causes a reduction in voltage).

A reference voltage is produced by the potential divider circuit which consists of R1, R3, and R4, and this is connected to the inverting (−) input of I.C.2. R3 can be used to vary this reference voltage, and in practice the voltage at the slider of this component is adjusted to the same potential as that produced across D1 when it is at the maximum acceptable temperature.

The output of I.C.2 will be high if the non-inverting input is at a lower voltage than the inverting input, and the output will go low if the comparative input states are transposed. Therefore under ordinary operating conditions the diode sensor will be below the alarm threshold temperature, and the voltage at the non-inverting input will be higher than the one fed to the inverting input. This will cause I.C.2 output to go high.

A silicon controlled switch is used as the relay driver, but in this case it is not used with the relay coil in its anode circuit and the input applied to its GK terminal. Instead, the relay coil is connected in the cathode circuit and the input voltage is applied to the GA terminal. The device still operates as a very sensitive thrysistor, but it is necessary to take the GA terminal about 0.5 volts negative with respect to the anode in order to trigger the device into the "on" state.

Under normal circumstances the GA terminal of I.C.3 will be held at virtually the same potential as the anode terminal by the output of I.C.2. However, if D1 should go above the threshold temperature, it will supply a voltage to the non-inverting input of I.C.2 which is lower than that appearing at its inverting input. This will result in the output going low, and the coupling via R5 will result in the GA terminal of I.C.3 being taken sufficiently positive to switch the device on. Once triggered, it will latch in the "on" state and the relay will be energised until the supply is disconnected using on/off switch S1.

The voltage used to supply the reference voltage circuit and the diode sensor circuit must be extremely well stabilised. It must be remembered that the voltage across the diode only alters by a very few millivolts per degree Centigrade change, and so only a very small change in the supply potential is needed in order to significantly change the input voltages to I.C.2, and thus alter the threshold temperature of the device.

I.C.1 is a small monolithic I.C. voltage regulator and this provides an extremely high degree of stabilisation at its output. C1 is needed in order to aid the stability of I.C.1.

C2 is the compensation capacitor for I.C.2, and D2 is the protective diode which is normally fitted across a relay coil which is driven from a semiconductor circuit. R6 is needed in order to prevent spurious triggering of the circuit.


## Construction

Most of the circuit is constructed on a 0.1in. pitch stripboard using the component layout shown in Fig. 33. The board is 14 copper strips by 20 holes and there are five breaks in the copper strips, as indicated in the diagram.

I.C.2 has a CMOS input stage which is vulnerable to damage by high static voltages and the same precautions as mentioned previously should be observed.

D1 can be mounted on the component panel along with the other components, but in many applications it will probably be desirable or even essential to have the sensor remotely located from the rest of the unit. This is perfectly acceptable, and an ordinary unscreened cable can normally be used to

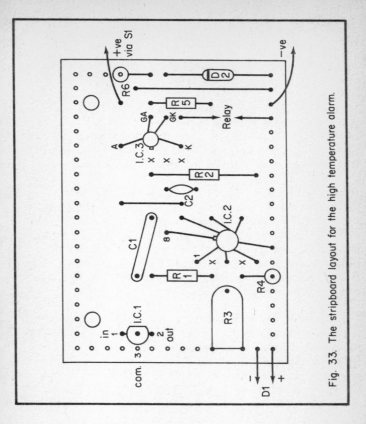

Fig. 33. The stripboard layout for the high temperature alarm.

connect the sensor to the main circuit. If the connecting
lead is very long, say more than about 8 metres or so, it might
be necessary to use screened cable as otherwise stray pick-up
in the cable could upset the operation of the circuit. If this
should be necessary, the outer braiding of the cable connects
to the negative supply rail of the main equipment and the cathode (+) connection of D1. The inner conductor connects to
D1 anode (−) and the non-inverting input of I.C.2. An alternative to using a screened lead is to add an electrolythic capacitor
of about 10mfd. in value in parallel with D1 (negative lead of
the capacitor connected to the negative supply rail).

87

The quiescent current consumption of the unit is about 5mA. from a 9 volt supply, and about 30mA. higher than this when the relay is activated. If preferred, the relay coil can be replaced by a small buzzer or electronic alarm generator, so that the unit directly operates the warning device.

In some applications, such as where the sensor diode will be immersed in a liquid, it will be necessary to house it in a probe of some kind. In most applications the finished installation will probably be somewhat neater if D1 is contained in a probe, even if the protection afforded by the probe is not needed.

A small test tube or a small tube-like plastic container will make an excellent basis for such a probe. One problem that will arise from mounting the sensor in a probe is that of insulation. The air between the diode and the container will tend to insulate the diode from the outside temperature and could make the unit rather slow at responding to temperature changes. It could even result in it failing to respond to all under certain conditions, thus rendering the equipment inoperative.

This can be overcome by putting a substance in the tube which is a good electrical conductor, but which is also a good conductor of heat. This will ensure a good thermal contact between the sensor diode and the outside environment, but will not affect the electrical operation of the unit. Silicon grease or a silicon grease substitute is a good choice for this application as it will provide excellent results, and will also protect the diode and wiring in the probe against corrosion.

### Adjustment

The circuit is capable of operating over a very wide temperature range, and the threshold temperature can be anything from well below 0 degrees Centigrade to more than 100 degrees Centigrade. The easiest way of giving R3 the correct setting is to place the sensor in an environment which is at the desired threshold temperature, and then starting with R3 in a fully clockwise direction, slowly and carefully adjust it in an anticlockwise direction just far enough to cause the relay to switch on, and no further.

As R3 has such a wide coverage it is difficult to adjust it to a very high degree of accuracy. In critical applications it would be advisable to replace this component with a multi-turn potentiometer, although these have the disadvantage of being extremely expensive. A cheaper alternative is to experimentally raise the values of R1 and R4. This will have the effect of reducing the range of temperatures covered by R3, but care must be taken not to bring the required threshold temperature outside the adjustment range of R3.

## Under-Temperature Alarm

It is an easy matter to convert the circuit of Fig. 32 to act as an under-temperature alarm, and the necessary modifications are shown in Fig.34. Only the output stage is altered, the other circuitry remaining exactly as before.

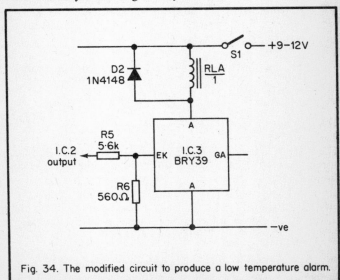

Fig. 34. The modified circuit to produce a low temperature alarm.

No additional components are required, and the modification consists of placing the relay in the anode circuit of I.C.3 rather than in its cathode circuit, and the input signal is applied to the GK terminal instead of the GA one. R6 is now connected between the gate and the negative supply rail, of course, so that it prevents spurious triggering of the output device.

When the unit is used as an under-temperature alarm, the voltage produced by the sensor diode will normally be less than set at R3 slider and fed to the inverting input of I.C.2. Under normal operating conditions, the voltage at the inverting input of I.C.2 will be higher than the voltage present at its non-inverting input, and this will cause the output of this device to assume the low state. The GK terminal of I.C.3 will thus be held at virtually the negative supply rail voltage, and so the device will not switch on.

If the sensor diode goes below the threshold temperature it will produce an output voltage which is in excess of that at the inverting input of I.C.2, and the output of the comparator will assume the high state. In doing so it will take the GK terminal of I.C.3 sufficiently positive to cause the device to turn on and activate the relay.

Thus the circuit action is altered to provide a low temperature alarm.


## Construction

The stripboard layout of Fig. 33 can easily be modified to accommodate the under-temperature circuit, and the necessary alterations are detailed in Fig. 35. Only the right hand portion of the board is changed, the majority of the layout remaining precisely as shown in Fig. 33. For this reason only the modified right hand section of the component panel has been illustrated in Fig. 35.

The notes on construction and adjustment of the high temperature alarm also apply to the under-temperature alarm in the main. However, the setting up procedure is slightly different. At the outset R3 should be adjusted in a fully anti-clockwise direction, and then with the sensor diode at the required threshold temperature, R3 is slowly adjusted in a clockwise direction just far enough to cause the relay to switch on.

When setting up either temperature alarm it is essential that the diode sensor is given time to assume the same temperature as the environment in which it is placed. This will probably take no more than a few tens of seconds, but it is advisable to allow somewhat longer just to be on the safe side.

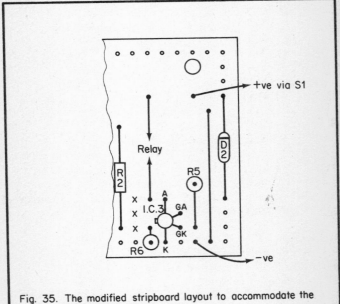

Fig. 35. The modified stripboard layout to accommodate the low temperature alarm.

## Components for High Temperature Alarm

**Resistors.** All ¼ watt 10% except R3.
R1        82k
R2        3.9k
R3        22k subminiature (0.1 watt) horizontal preset.
R4        8.2k
R5        5.6k
R6        560 ohms.

**Capacitors.**
C1        100nf type C280.
C2        56pf ceramic plate.

**Semiconductors.**
I.C.1.        $\mu$A78LO5WC, or similar 5 volt 100mA. voltage
              regulator.
I.C.2        CA3130T.
I.C.3        BRY39.
D1           1N4148.
D2           1N4148.

**Switch**
S1        S.P.S.T. toggle switch.

**Relay.**
Nominal 6 volt operation, coil resistance of about 185 ohms or more, and sufficient contacts of the correct type and adequate rating for the load(s) employed.

**Miscellaneous.**
0.1in. matrix stripboard panel.
Materials for probe (if required, see text).
Cases, connecting wire, solder, etc.

## Components for Low Temperature Alarm

Uses precisely the same components as high temperature alarm (see previous list).

## Baby Alarm/Doorphone

A baby alarm can be very useful since it enables the parents to listen for distress calls while they are not in the same room as the child, and perhaps engaged in some activity such as watching the T.V. or listening to the Hi-Fi, which could easily mask the direct sounds of distress calls.

There are two basic types of baby alarm; the type which sounds an audio alarm if it detects a sound level which is above a certain threshold volume, and the type which consists of a high gain amplifier fed from a microphone near the child and driving a speaker situated near the parents. The latter is probably the most satisfactory of the two sorts, and it is a device of this type which is described here.

The amplifier used in the device is also suitable for other purposes, such as in a doorphone system. This type of equipment is useful for determining just who the caller is before actually opening the door, and enables unwanted callers to be dealt with without any significant inconvenience being caused. Such a device can also be of considerable benefit to someone who is handicapped or is an invalid.

The circuit has good sensitivity and quality, and offers a high level of intelligibility provided reasonably good quality loudspeakers are employed. The output power is about 350mW. r.m.s. max. (16 ohm impedance speaker) which is more than adequate for most normal requirements.

Apart from use as a baby alarm or doorphone, the unit can be adapted for use as an intercom if desired, and if fed from a telephone pick-up coil it will even make a good telephone amplifier.

## The Circuit

The complete circuit diagram of the baby alarm is given in Fig. 36. An ordinary loudspeaker is used as the microphone

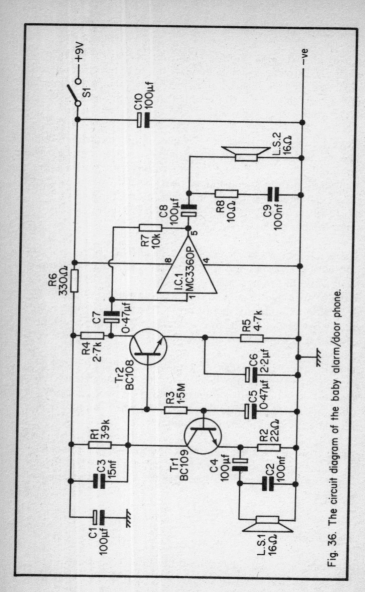

Fig. 36. The circuit diagram of the baby alarm/door phone.

94

and it acts as a crude type of moving coil microphone.

The output from the microphone (L.S.1) is at a very low amplitude, being very much less than 1mV. under normal operating conditions. The amplifier must therefore have a considerable degree of voltage amplification if a realistic volume level is to be obtained from the unit. In order to obtain good results from a loudspeaker used as a microphone it is also necessary for the amplifier to have a low input impedance.

Tr1 and Tr2 are connected in a direct coupled high gain compound amplifier configuration with Tr1 connected in the common base mode and Tr2 being used in the common emitter mode. A common base stage is the obvious choice for the input stage as it offers high voltage gain and a low input impedance which will provide a good match for the microphone. R1 is the collector load resistor for Tr1 and R3 provides the necessary biasing. R2 is the emitter resistor across which the input must be connected, and C5 provides decoupling at Tr1 base. C4 merely provides d.c. blocking at the input.

The bias voltage for Tr2 base is obtained from the collector of Tr1, and R5 is the emitter bias resistor for Tr2. C6 is the bypass capacitor for R5. The output of the amplifier is developed across R4 which is the collector load resistor for Tr2. Since both Tr1 and Tr2 have quite high voltage gains, the overall voltage amplification of the input amplifier is extremely high, and in normal use the signal level at Tr2 collector will be a few hundred millivolts peak to peak.

Because of this the output stage only needs to provide a comparatively modest amount of voltage amplification, and is primarily needed in order to provide buffering at the output. so that a loudspeaker can be properly driven by the circuit.

An MC3360P I.C. audio power amplifier is used in the output stage, and this consists basically of a conventional complementary emitter follower output stage and common emitter driver stage. It also contains the necessary circuitry to provide a small quiescent current through the output transistors, and to thermally stabilise this current so that there is no danger of thermal runaway occurring. This quiescent current is needed in order to reduce cross-over distortion to an insignificant level.

The MC3360P requires very little in the way of discrete circuitry. d.c. blocking capacitors are required at the input and output of the device, and these are C7 and C8 respectively. The MC3360P does not incorporate any overall biasing, and R7 is needed to bias the output to the usual level of approximately half the supply rail voltage.

R8 and C9 are needed in order to compensate for the fact that a loudspeaker offers an inductive impedance which therefore rises with increasing frequency. This can lead to instability, although in many cases these two components will not be essential to the correct functioning of the circuit.

With this type of equipment it is necessary for either the microphone or the loudspeaker to be remotely located from the rest of the unit, and it is normally the microphone that is situated away from the rest of the unit (although there is no reason for not having the loudspeaker remotely situated if preferred). With the microphone mounted away from the rest of the unit there is inevitably going to be a long microphone cable, and unless expensive screened cable is used there is a strong possibility that radio signals will be picked up in this cable at sufficient strength to produce a significant amount of breakthrough at the output. This problem is particularly acute during the hours of darkness.

The r.f. filtering provided by C2 and C3 should be adequate to totally eliminate any radio interference, but if necessary, they can be raised somewhat in value to provide further attenuation of r.f. signals.

Although the circuit has an extremely high overall level of gain, the supply decoupling provided by C1, R6 and C10 is more than adequate. S1 is the on/off switch. The quiescent current consumption of the circuit is 5mA., but the

MC3360P has a Class B output stage and so the current consumption rises considerably on high output volume levels, and can have a mean level of as much as 50mA. or so.

## Doorphone Switching

If the amplifier is employed in a doorphone system it will be necessary to include send/receive switching in the unit. This only requires the addition of a two pole change over switch which is connected into the system as shown in the skeleton circuit of Fig. 37.

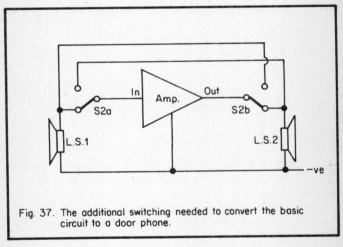

Fig. 37. The additional switching needed to convert the basic circuit to a door phone.

Now both speakers have to act as microphones and as speakers, and L.S.1 must be the remotely located speaker/microphone. The diagram shows S2 in the 'receive' position with L.S.1 connected to the input and acting as the microphone, and L.S.2 connected to the output and acting as the loudspeaker. This enables the caller to talk to the person inside the house. Putting S2 into the other position connects L.S.1 to the output and L.S.2 to the input, and thus reverses the roles of the speaker microphones. This enables the person inside the house to talk back to the caller.

Doorphones sometimes incorporate a call circuit, but it is easier to use the existing doorbell or doorknocker, and it has been assumed here that this is what will be done. Connecting the input to the output of the amplifier via a resistor of between about 100 ohms and a few k ohms in value will cause the circuit to oscillate and produce an audio tone from the speaker. However, for this to work in practice it would be necessary to ensure that the unit was always left in the 'receive' position by using a biased switch for S2, and the bell push would have to connect power to the circuit as well as providing the feedback to produce oscillation. Even then the volume from the unit would probably be much lower than that provided by an ordinary doorbell or doorknocker. It is therefore far more practical to simply retain the existing doorbell or doorknocker.

## Construction

Most of the components are accommodated on a 0.1 in. pitch stripboard panel which has 16 copper strips by 28 holes, and details of this are provided in Fig. 38. There are only four breaks in the copper strips and three link wires, and care should be taken not to omit any of these. It is also important that no errors are made in the wiring, and that no accidental short circuits are made between adjacent copper strips with small blobs of excess solder, particularly around I.C.1. In either case the result could possibly be damage to I.C.1 when the unit is connected to a power source. Incidentally, I.C.1 is housed in a standard 8 pin DIL plastic package, but note that there are no internal connections to pins 2, 3, 6, and 7.

The input cable can be any thin two way cable, such as bell wire or sub-miniature twin core mains cable. For minimal stay pick-up of mains hum etc. in the microphone cable, a screened type should be used (outer braiding to the negative supply rail of the unit, and the inner conductor to C4 negative), but this is not essential and satisfactory results should be obtained using ordinary two way cable, even if the input cable is many metres long. The prototype has been tested using a microphone cable about 14 metres long, but the unit should

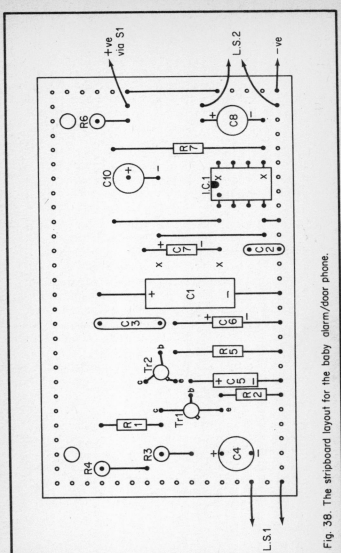

Fig. 38. The stripboard layout for the baby alarm/door phone.

function properly using a cable considerably longer than this.

The ideal impedance for the speaker/microphones is 16 ohms, but unfortunately speakers of this impedance are not very widely available. In practice the circuit would seem to work well using any speaker impedance of between 8 and 35 ohms. The circuit will work with higher impedance speakers, but this results in a considerable reduction in the maximum available output power (only about 70mW. into an 80 ohm load for instance). For this reason it is advisable to regard 35 ohms as the upper limit on the speaker impedance. Speakers having an impedance of less than 8 ohms should not be used as this could result in considerable overloading of I.C.1 and consequent damage to this device.

Probably the best speaker size to use is about 66 to 75mm. in diameter. Smaller speakers tend to give rather poor volume and frequency response, and will probably not be capable of handling the maximum available output power anyway. Larger speakers generally give better volume and frequency response when used as speakers, but are not recommended for this application as they do not usually provide very good results when utilized as microphones, there is usually such a loss of treble response that speech becomes almost unintelligible.

If R8 and C9 prove to be necessary, they are wired direct across L.S.2, or from the wiper of S2b to the negative supply rail if the unit is used as a doorphone or an intercom.

Mounting these components on the component panel could easily make the instability worse rather than better. If instability does occur, it will probably manifest itself as a roughness of quality on medium and high level outputs, rather than in the form of actual oscillation. The addition of R8 and C9 should completely clear up the problem.

## Components for Baby Alarm/Doorphone

**Resistors.** All ¼ watt 10%.

| | |
|---|---|
| R1 | 3.9k |
| R2 | 22 ohms |
| R3 | 1.5 Meg. |
| R4 | 2.7k |
| R5 | 4.7k |
| R6 | 330 ohms |
| R7 | 10k |
| R8 | 10 ohms |

**Capacitors.**

| | |
|---|---|
| C1 | 100mfd. 10v.w. |
| C2 | 100nf type C280. |
| C3 | 15nf type C280. |
| C4 | 100mfd. 10v.w. |
| C5 | 0.47mfd. 10v.w. |
| C6 | 2.2mfd. 10v.w. |
| C7 | 0.47mfd. 10v.w. |
| C8 | 100mfd. 10v.w. |
| C9 | 100nf. type C280. |
| C10 | 100mfd. 10v.w. |

**Semiconductors**

| | |
|---|---|
| Tr1 | BC109. |
| Tr2 | BC108. |
| I.C.1. | MC3360P. |

**Switches**

| | |
|---|---|
| S1 | S.P.S.T. toggle type. |
| S2 | D.P.D.T. toggle type (only needed for doorphone). |

**Speakers.**

| | |
|---|---|
| L.S.1. | 8 to 35 ohm impedance speaker, about 66 to 75 mm. diameter. |
| L.S.2. | Same type as above. |

**Miscellaneous.**
0.1in. matrix stripboard panel.
Cases, connecting wire, solder, etc.

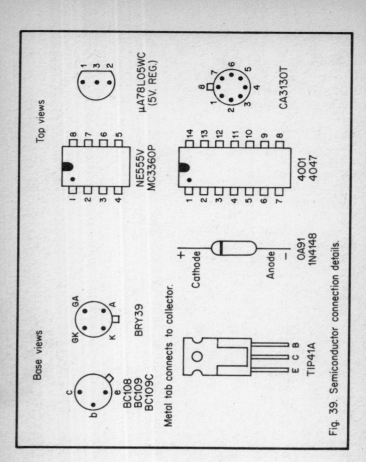

Fig. 39. Semiconductor connection details.

*Notes*

*Notes*

**222: SOLID STATE SHORT WAVE RECEIVERS FOR BEGINNERS**
**AUTHOR: R.A. PENFOLD**                          PRICE: £1.95
ISBN: 0 900162 62 7                                    96 Pages
Approx. Size: 180 x 105 mm

There is a strange fascination in listening to a broadcast which has been transmitted from a station that may be many thousands of miles away across the other side of the world. This has helped to make short wave listening one of the most popular and interesting branches of electronics and for this reason, is an excellent way of capturing the interest of a beginner. In fact, very many enthusiasts and "Hams" have been introduced to the hobby in this way.

In this book, Mr R.A. Penfold, who is a very experienced author and has regularly written for many of the popular electronic monthly magazines, has designed and developed several modern solid state short wave receiver circuits that will give a fairly high level of performance, despite the fact that they use only relatively few and inexpensive components.

**223: 50 PROJECTS USING IC CA3130**
**AUTHOR: R.A. PENFOLD**                          PRICE: £1.25
ISBN: 0 900162 65 1                                    112 Pages
Approx. Size: 180 x 105 mm

The CA3130 is currently one of the more advanced operational amplifiers that is available to the home constructor. This means that it is often capable of a higher level of performance than many other devices and that it often needs fewer ancillary components.

In this book, the author has designed and developed a number of interesting and useful projects which are divided into five general categories:

I    –    Audio Projects
II   –    R.F. Projects
III  –    Test Equipment
IV   –    Household Projects
V    –    Miscellaneous Projects

An ideal book for both the beginner and more advance enthusiast alike.

**224: 50 CMOS IC PROJECTS**
**AUTHOR: R.A. PENFOLD**                          PRICE: £2.50
ISBN: 0 900162 64 3                                    112 Pages
Approx. Size: 180 x 105 mm

CMOS IC's are probably the most versatile range of digital devices for use by the amateur enthusiast. They are suitable for an extraordinary wide range of applications and are now also some of the most inexpensive and easily available types of IC.

Mr R.A. Penfold has designed and developed a number of interesting and useful projects which are divided into four general categories:

I   – Multivibrators
II  – Amplifiers and Oscillators
III – Trigger Devices
IV  – Special Devices

A must for any electronic enthusiast's library.

## 226: HOW TO BUILD ADVANCED SHORT WAVE RECEIVERS

AUTHOR: R.A. PENFOLD                                  PRICE: £2.50
ISBN: 0 900162 67 8                                      128 Pages
Approx. Size: 180 x 105 mm

Although many short wave listeners and radio amateurs use commercial equipment these days, greater satisfaction and enjoyment can be gained from the hobby by using home constructed equipment. Using ready made S.W. gear does not give any insight into the way the apparatus functions and by building one's own equipment, it is virtually inevitable that a reasonable understanding of the techniques involved will be grasped. Obviously, such an understanding is very helpful when it comes to actually using a finished receiver, and it should enable the operator to obtain optimum results from the set. In this book, Mr R.A. Penfold gives full practical constructional details of a number of receivers which should have levels of performance at least equal to that of commercially built sets of similar complexity. Furthermore, the home constructed receiver is likely to cost very much less than it's ready made equivalent.

Also included are a number of add-on circuits, such as Q-Multiplier, S-Meter, Noise Limiter, etc., which can be used to aid and improve reception when using the receivers.

## 227: BEGINNERS GUIDE TO BUILDING ELECTRONIC PROJECTS

AUTHOR: R.A. PENFOLD                                  PRICE: £1.95
ISBN: 0 900162 68 6                                      112 Pages
Approx. Size: 180 x 105 mm

The purpose of this book is to enable the complete beginner to tackle the practical side of electronics, so that he or she can confidently build the electronic projects that are regularly featured in the popular magazines and books.

Subjects such as component identification, tools, soldering, various constructional methods (Matrixboard, Veroboard, P.C.B.) cases, legends etc. are covered in details and practical examples in the form of simple projects are given.

Written by Mr R.A. Penfold who is a very experienced author of many books and who also writes regularly for the popular electronics magazines.

An absolutely invaluable book for all beginners in electronics.

## BP45: PROJECTS IN OPTO-ELECTRONICS
## AUTHOR: R.A. PENFOLD
ISBN: 0 85934 049 X

PRICE: £1.95
112 Pages

Approx. Size: 180 x 105 mm

Any electronic or electrical device that responds to light may be considered to come under the heading of Opto-Electronic devices.

Although many people tend to take Opto-Electronic devices and circuits for granted, it is hoped that this book will show even the most experienced reader that they can be used in a surprisingly wide range of applications.

The purpose of this book is to describe a number of projects which may be of interest to all electronics enthusiasts. Included are simple circuits using ordinary light emitting diodes (L.E.D.s) as well as more sophisticated designs such as Infra Red Transmitters and Detectors, Modulated Light Transmission and also Photographic projects etc.


## BP49: POPULAR ELECTRONIC PROJECTS
## AUTHOR: R.A. PENFOLD
ISBN: 0 85934 053 8

PRICE: £2.50
144 Pages

Approx. Size: 180 x 105 mm

Another book by the well known author – Mr. R.A. Penfold – which includes a collection of the most popular types of circuits and projects which, we feel sure, will provide a number of designs to interest most electronics constructors.

The projects selected cover a very wide range and are divided into four basic types: Radio Projects, Audio Projects, Household Projects and Test Equipment.

All the projects use modern, inexpensive and freely available components.

A useful book for all those interested in Electronics.


## BP59: SECOND BOOK OF CMOS IC PROJECTS
## AUTHOR: MR. R.A. PENFOLD
ISBN: 0 900162 78 3

PRICE: £1.50
128 Pages

Approx. Size: 180 x 105 mm

In 1977 we published Mr. Penfold's book No. 224 "50 CMOS IC PROJECTS" which proved to be extremely popular and although that book covered a very wide range of projects, it by no means included all the possible uses of CMOS devices.

The aim of the Second Book is to provide a further selection of useful circuits, mainly of a fairly simple nature, and therefore within the capabilities of both the beginner and more advanced constructor.

The contents of the Second Book have been selected to produce a minimum of overlap between the two books and the versatility of CMOS devices is such that there is no problem in achieving this.

Please note overleaf is a list of other titles that are available in our range of Radio and Electronics Books.

These should be available from most good Booksellers, Radio Component Dealers and Mail Order Companies.

However, should you experience difficulty in obtaining any title in your area, then please write directly to the publishers enclosing payment to cover the cost of the book plus adequate postage.

If you would like a copy of our latest catalogue of Radio & Electronics Books then please send a Stamped Addressed Envelope to:—

BERNARD BABANI (publishing) LTD
The Grampians
Shepherds Bush Road
London W6 7NF
England